Flexible Manufacturing Technologies and International Competitiveness

Flexible Manufacturing Technologies and International Competitiveness

Joseph Tidd

Pinter Publishers, London

First published in Great Britain in 1991 by
Pinter Publishers Limited
25 Floral Street, London WC2E 9DS

British Library Cataloguing in Publication Data

A CIP catalogue record for this book is available from the
British Library
ISBN 0 86187 103 0

For enquiries in North America please contact
PO Box 197, Irvington, NY 10533

A CIP catalog record of this book is available
from the Library of Congress

Typeset by Witwell Ltd, Southport.
Printed and bound in Great Britain by Billings and Son Ltd, Worcester.

Contents

List of figures

List of tables

Acknowledgements

Much of the research upon which this book is based was conducted while I worked at the Science Policy Research Unit (SPRU), University of Sussex, UK. I wish to thank numerous colleagues at SPRU, Jamie Fleck of the University of Edinburgh and Professor Chris Voss of London Business School for helping to focus my initial ideas into a practical project. I must also thank all the companies and organisations throughout the UK and Japan which participated in the study. I am particularly grateful to Professor Kazuo Yamafuji and Professor Hiroshi Makino for their invaluable help in Japan.

I am in debt to Professor Dan Jones of Cardiff Business School for his continuous support and enthusiasm, and Professor Keith Pavitt of SPRU and Professor John Bessant of Brighton Business School for their constructive and encouraging comments on earlier drafts of this work. The views expressed in this book are my own, and are not necessarily those of the Confederation of British Industry (CBI).

1
Introduction

1.1 Technology and competitiveness

'Automate or liquidate' was the maxim of the 1980s. The most successful manufacturing economies, notably Japan, were also those that made the greatest investment in advanced manufacturing technologies (AMT). However, it is extremely difficult to unravel cause from effect in such cases, and a growing number of firms have become sceptical of the benefits of AMT. In the United States 'many companies tossed millions of dollars' worth of fancy equipment into their factories and wound up with little to show for it' (*Business Week*, 8 May 1989); in the United Kingdom the use of robots and flexible manufacturing systems has been restricted and these technologies are 'now accepted as being hard to integrate and even more difficult to cost justify' (*Industrial Computing*, October 1989). Companies like General Motors installed thousands of the latest robots and machine vision systems during the 1980s but failed to match Japanese competitors in terms of productivity or quality.

Nevertheless, most manufacturers have not rejected AMT, but believe that robots, flexible manufacturing systems, and other 'islands of automation' are simply not enough. Major American and European companies are banking on the next generation of technology to provide the answers in the 1990s, so-called 'smart' factories based on developments in artificial intelligence and fully computer-integrated manufacture (CIM). Marxists such as Michel Aglietta (1979) and André Gorz (1982, 1985) write of a technological 'revolution' and the 'crisis' of mass production resulting in a transition from Fordism to Neo-Fordism characterised by more flexible production and fragmented demand. More recently, management gurus like Tom Peters (1987) and Michael Porter (1989) talk of the declining importance of scale economies, and the growth of flexible factories serving multi-niche markets. In short there is a growing consensus that technological developments and market trends are converging. It is less clear what the outcome will be.

In their influential but controversial work Piore and Sabel (1984) argue that 'flexible specialisation' will replace mass production, and technologically dynamic smaller firms using craft practices will challenge larger manufacturers. Others also believe that the greatest impact of AMT will be in batch production, and will therefore improve the competitiveness of small and medium-sized manufacturers (Ayres & Miller, 1981; Kaplinsky, 1984). Alternatively, larger manufacturers may continue to dominate those industries currently characterised by mass production provided they exploit the flexibility of the new technologies, but 'economies of scope' will become more important than 'economies of 'scale' (Goldhar & Jelinek, 1983; Ergas, 1984). Clearly considerable uncertainty still exists, and a recent review of the evidence to date concluded that: 'there appears to be no dominant pattern of introduction of these technologies into the economy and society as a whole, neither at the "macro" level, nor, for what we understand, from more microeconomic indicators' (Arcangeli *et al.*, 1987, p.21).

1.2 Emerging trends

It is increasingly difficult to support the argument that this ambiguity is due to the immaturity of the technology. Numerically controlled machine tools, flexible machining systems, and robots were first developed in the 1950s and 1960s and applications have grown rapidly since the late 1970s. And yet no international patterns of development or adoption of AMT have emerged after more than ten years of diffusion. This may be because such technologies are inherently adaptable, and therefore different organisational and market contexts could result in divergent paths of development and adoption.

Case studies appear to support this proposition, and concepts such as 'design space' (Bessant, 1983) and 'strategic choice' (Buchanan & Boddy, 1983) have been used to describe the range of options available. It has been suggested that technologies such as robotic and flexible machining systems are essentially 'configurational', and that mutually interacting (but not necessarily mutually constraining) components may be deployed in a very wide, possibly arbitrary, range of ways (Fleck, 1987a). Recent research confirms that the management and implementation of AMT affect the performance of the technology, and suggests that distinct national trends may be emerging (Jaikumar, 1986; Voss, 1988). This book examines such trends and attempts to identify current international 'best practice'.

There is overwhelming evidence that Japanese manufacturers are making more effective use of AMT than their American and European competitors. Clearly, Japanese plants have many more NCMT, FMS, and robots, but this obvious quantitative disparity is perhaps less significant than less apparent qualitative differences in the development and application of such technologies. Japanese suppliers and users of AMT have consistently developed and adopted less sophisticated systems than their counterparts in the West. American and European manufacturers have concentrated on more complex and expensive technology in an effort to overcome organisational shortcomings and match Japanese levels of productivity and quality. But advanced manufacturing technology and flexibility are not synonymous.

While users of AMT in the West have been preoccupied with reducing costs and improving quality, Japanese manufacturers have been busy increasing their flexibility. They are now beginning to achieve flexible but efficient production based on the extensive application of relatively simple programmable automation. More product variants are produced per plant, and product life cycles are much shorter than in the United States or Europe, despite the use of less sophisticated technology. This suggests that manufacturers in the West may begin to match the costs and quality of their Japanese competitors in the 1990s, to find that the rules have changed and that they are ill equipped to compete on the basis of low-cost, flexible production (Ferdows *et al.*, 1986). This book examines how the context of development and adoption of NCMT, flexible machining systems, and industrial robots has resulted in divergent paths, and assesses the strategic implications of current trends in manufacturing flexibility.

1.3 Structure of the book

Chapter 2 identifies the market and technological imperatives for greater manufacturing flexibility. On the one hand, increased competition in traditional mass markets and growing consumer prosperity demand more product variety and shorter product life cycles. On the other, more easily programmable technologies such as NCMT, FMS and industrial robots promise to be more flexible than previous forms of automation. Chapter 3 examines the significance of flexibility in manufacturing, in particular the traditional trade-offs between economies of scale and scope, and static and dynamic efficiencies: the so-called 'productivity dilemma'. The main forms and determinants of flexibility are identified, including the role of technology.

International patterns of development and adoption of NCMT, FMS, and robots are examined in Chapter 4. Previous studies have failed to identify any dominant trend, but a detailed breakdown by country, sector, and size reveals that distinct national patterns are emerging. However, the impact on flexibility has been limited. Chapter 5 focuses on the growing application of robots to assembly, and the various options available to users. Assembly has traditionally represented an automation bottleneck, but now manufacturers worldwide are beginning to adopt robotic assembly. Choices made now may have serious long-term implications. Subsequent chapters contrast the experience of users in the UK and Japan.

British manufacturers have been slow to adopt such technology compared to all their major competitors overseas. Perhaps more significantly, current users have chosen to adopt state-of-the-art technology, but in most cases have failed to improve their competitiveness. Chapter 6 examines some of the reasons for this. In contrast Japanese manufacturers have made massive investment in AMT and in many sectors lead the world in terms of productivity and quality. But the relationship between AMT and competitiveness is more complex. Chapter 7 argues that Japanese manufacturers achieved the greatest improvements in productivity and quality before the widespread adoption of AMT, but that such technologies are now contributing towards a strategy of low-cost, flexible production.

The final chapter brings together the most significant market and technological trends and assesses the implications if manufacturers in Japan and the West continue to pursue divergent paths. The Japanese approach clearly represents current international best practice, and suggests that CIM and flexible manufacturing may not be synonymous. If the next generation of 'smart' factories are unable to overcome the productivity dilemma many American and European manufacturers will find themselves ill equipped to face the Japanese challenge in the 1990s.

2
Technological and market imperatives

2.1 Technological and Market Pressures

There is a growing consensus that the principal market and technological pressures on manufacturing in the 1990s are complementary, and that both 'market pull' and 'technology push' are forcing international best practice towards greater flexibility. Marxist writers highlight the saturation and growing uncertainty of traditional mass markets (Aglietta, 1979; Gorz, 1985); management texts stress the need to respond to the demands of more affluent customers and multiple-niche markets (Goldhar & Jelinek, 1983; Peters, 1987). Academic work has concentrated on the technological imperatives, in particular the impact of programmable automation such as flexible machining systems (FMS) and industrial robots (Dosi, 1986; Freeman & Perez, 1988). The interaction of these trends represent a formidable challenge to manufacturers in the 1990s (Figure 2.1).

There is little disagreement concerning the significance of these market and technological trends, but the implications for manufacturers are less clear. The management literature is unanimous: the 'winners' in the 1990s will be smaller, more specialised, focused factories competing on the basis of quality and responsiveness in niche markets (Peters, 1987; PA Consulting Group, 1990). Similarly, in their influential but controversial work Piore and Sabel argue that:

what is distinctive about the current crisis is that the shift toward greater flexibility is provoking technological sophistication rather than regression to simple techniques. As firms have faced the need to redesign products and methods to address rising costs and growing competition, they have found new ways to cut the cost of customised production. And the more they have narrowed the gap between mass and craft production, the easier it has become to draw customers away from the formerly cheaper mass produced goods. Technological dynamism has allowed a shift from a purely reactive strategy, aimed at survival, to an expansive strategy, which has threatened to cut the ground away from mass production. (1984, p. 207)

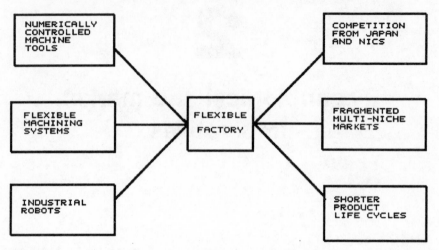

Figure 2.1 Technological and market trends towards greater flexibility in the 1990s

But the evidence to date is ambiguous. Some research does suggest that programmable automation will have the greatest impact in batch production, making SMEs more competitive with larger, high-volume manufacturers (Ayres & Miller, 1985; Kaplinsky, 1984). However, other work indicates that such technologies may instead allow large companies to exploit 'economies of scope' and threaten SMEs in niche markets (Goldhar & Jelinek, 1983; Ergas, 1984).

2.2 Market trends

The Single European Market has attracted a great deal of attention in recent years, but this simply reflects the wider trend towards a global market. World trade has consistently grown faster than GDP since the 1950s, demonstrating the growing liberalisation of international markets and interdependence of national economies. In the 1970s Japan emerged as a world leader in the manufacture of cars and other consumer durables, followed by the Asian NICs. During the 1980s the NIC economies grew more than twice as fast as the industrialised nations, other than Japan, and in most cases this rapid growth has been export-led: exports from South Korea, Taiwan, and Hong Kong grew by more than 10 per cent every year. Manufacturers from such low-cost countries have become major players in mass markets as diverse as clothing and video recorders, and are now attempting to move into semiconductors and other higher value-added products (Hoffman, 1989). But there is evidence that this cost advantage will be less important in the 1990s.

Greater affluence and the example set by Japanese manufacturers have increased the expectations of consumers in the mature economies, and non-

Table 2.1 Proliferation of models and body styles at Nissan in Japan, 1965–1988

Year	Number of models	Number of body styles
1965	5	5
1970	8	10
1975	10	22
1980	16	36
1988	24	50

Source: Yamauchi, 1988

price factors have become increasingly significant. In the 1980s customers began to demand higher-quality products, and more recently greater choice and performance. Manufacturers in Japan have not simply responded to such trends, but have also helped to create them. As a result, they continue to increase their share of world exports, despite the high yen and labour costs comparable with those in the United States. This highlights the limitations of a manufacturing strategy based only on market research. As noted by Penrose:

'expectations' and not 'objective facts' are the immediate determinants of firm behaviour, although there may be a relationship between expectations and 'facts' — indeed there must be if action is to be successful . . . in the last analysis the 'environment' rejects or confirms the soundness of the judgements about it, but the relevant environment is not an objective fact discoverable before the event; economists cannot predict it unless they can predict the ways in which a firm's actions will themselves 'change' the relevant environment in the future. (1968, p. 41)

A survey of manufacturers in Japan illustrates the trend toward greater variety. Between 1981 and 1984 over half increased their product range by up to 20 per cent, and a quarter by 20–50 per cent (Economic Research Institute, 1985, p. 10). This trend is apparent across all sectors, including those traditionally thought of as offering commodity-type products. During the 1980s Nissan increased its model range by 50 per cent, from 16 to 24, and the total number of body styles from 36 to 50 (Table 2.1). In contrast many manufacturers in the West followed the advice of leading management gurus such as Skinner (1978, 1985), and 'focused' production in order to reduce complexity and cut costs. In Europe, Fiat continued to produce just nine different models, and the number of bodies was actually reduced from nine to six between 1980 and 1987 (Fiat Auto S.p.a, 1987); and Ford continues to develop its 'world car' strategy.

The diversity of products manufactured in Japan is not simply the result of cosmetic variation, nor trivial product differentiation. In most cases it reflects product ranges designed to capture several niche markets. Manufacturers have exploited the opportunity for more complex, technology-based products, and the demand for these has grown much faster than for traditional commodity items. Research confirms that the competitiveness of many consumer durables increases sharply as additional features are added (Swann & Taghavi, 1988). Japanese manufacturers have built on their reputation for quality products, and are continuously moving 'upmarket', competing on the basis of technological innovation and so-called 'knowledge-intensive' products.

This strategy has always represented international best practice in science-based industries such as chemicals and pharmaceuticals, but product innovation has only recently become important again in 'mature' sectors like automobile manufacture. In these industries the focus has traditionally been on process innovation and the efficiency of production. It has been argued that once a dominant product design has become established, attention shifts from product to process, and radical product innovation becomes more difficult as production efficiency increases — the so-called 'productivity dilemma' (Abernathy, 1978). This was clearly the case in the United States up to the 1980s, but may no longer be an appropriate model for Japanese manufacturers in the 1990s.

In Japan continuous product innovation or *kaizen* is commonplace in many sectors considered 'mature', and consequently life cycles have become shorter. This trend is particularly strong in 'high-tech' industries like consumer electronics, but is also significant in others (Table 2.2).

In the United Kingdom product life cycles tend to be much longer (Table 2.3). More than half of UK manufacturers expect no change in product life cycles, and just a quarter anticipate any reduction in the life of their products (CBI, 1990). In contrast Japanese manufacturers are simultaneously reducing product development times and life cycles. For example, it typically takes an American or European automobile company six to seven years to develop a new model, but Japanese manufacturers have cut their average lead time to four years, and at Honda it is just three (Karlsson & Carlsson, 1989).

In short, manufacturers in the United States and Europe can no longer compete with low-cost countries in traditional mass markets. During the 1970s many manufacturers located 'off shore' in order to exploit the cost advantages of the NICs. The trend towards more product variety and short lead times and life cycles — the increasing complexity of production — questions the wisdom of this strategy. Many manufacturers have made massive investments in advanced manufacturing technologies (AMT) in an effort to overcome these problems, and to match the quality and flexibility of their Japanese competitors.

2.3 Technological trajectories

In the management literature the relationship between manufacturing technology and markets is typically presented as a question of matching

Table 2.2 Trends in product life cycles in Japan, 1981–1985

Industry	Life cycle (years)	Percentage of products	
		1981	1985
Electrical engineering	0–1	3	8
	1–2	18	26
	2–3	11	29
	3–5	25	16
	5+	43	21
Motor vehicles	0–1	7	7
	1–2	7	10
	2–3	10	28
	3–5	32	17
	5+	44	38
Mechanical engineering	0–1	4	3
	1–2	3	7
	2–3	4	29
	3–5	32	22
	5+	57	39
All industry	0–1	4	6
	1–2	9	15
	2–3	9	26
	3–5	28	19
	5+	50	34

Source: Economic Research Institute, 1985.

product and process characteristics. Any manufacturer will normally operate in a specific region of the product/process matrix, and most will occupy the diagonal (Figure 2.2). Clearly, a capital goods manufacturer, characterised by low-volume, complex production, requires versatile, high-performance manufacturing technology; a manufacturer of consumer durables, producing a limited range of high-volume products needs more efficient and less flexible manufacturing systems. Companies which operate outside the 'normal' diagonal region are likely to experience difficulties in coordinating their manufacturing technology and product markets, but in some cases may gain a competitive advantage (Hayes and Wheelwright, 1979).

Empirical evidence supports this model. Data from the 1977 US Census of Production has been used to identify the dominant mode of production in different industries (Miller, 1985). This clearly demonstrates the significance of mass production in the automobile industry, and batch production in the general machinery sector (Table 2.4). However, it probably

Table 2.3 Trends in product life cycles in the UK, 1989

Industry	Life cycle (years)	Percentage of products
Electrical engineering	0–1	0
	1–2	3
	2–3	13
	3–5	47
	5+	36
Motor vehicles	0–1	0
	1–2	14
	2–3	0
	3–5	14
	5+	71
Mechanical engineering	0–1	0
	1–2	0
	2–3	0
	3–5	31
	5+	69
All industry	0–1	3
	1–2	4
	2–3	8
	3–5	30
	5+	55

Source: CBI, 1990.

underestimates the importance of mass production in the electrical sector for several reasons: calculations were based on the amount of metal, not materials processed; only half of all product types in the electrical sector were included; and imports of electrical goods are very high in the United States. Nevertheless, it does confirm a general relationship between products and process, and thus markets and technology.

This provides a useful 'snapshot' of the United States in the 1970s, but markets and technology are not static. The automobile industry, the archetype mass producer, has undergone many transitions: from the first, and arguably only, manufacturer of a high-volume, completely standardised product in the United States up to the 1930s; increased emphasis on product innovation and differentiation in the 1950s and 1960s, particularly in Europe; greater attention to the organisation and management of production during the 1970s and 1980s following the emergence of the Japanese; and most recently production in low factor cost locations and the widespread application of flexible manufacturing technologies (Abernathy *et al.*, 1983, 1985, pp.99–118; Altshuler *et al.*, pp.11–45).

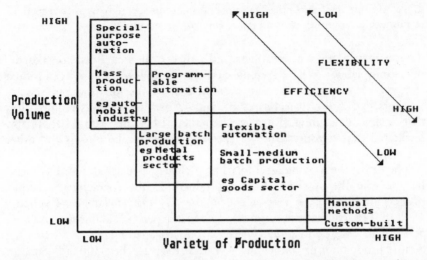

Figure 2.2 Typical relationship between manufacturing technology and type of production

Table 2.4 Mode of production by sector in the US

Mode of production	Percentage of output of sector				
	Metal	Mach.	Elec.	Trans.	All
Custom	1	36	55	20	25
Batch	70	64	35	8	43
Mass	29	0	10	72	36

Source: Miller, 1985, p. 183.

It has been argued that 'the American economy grew not by evolving, but by taking its basic style of production to its limits: — ever larger volumes of standardised goods at ever lower unit costs' (Reich, 1983, p. 11). This is clearly an overstatement, but during the nineteenth century the use of special-purpose machine tools to achieve interchangeable parts was known as the 'American system' in Europe (Rosenberg, 1976, p. 120). But such techniques were not widespread even in the United States, and were confined to the manufacture of expensive, high value-added products until Ford adopted them. Ford was not the first to apply the 'American system' to the manufacture of automobiles, but according to Hounshell:

the rise of Ford marks an entirely new epoch in the manufacture of consumer durables in America. The Ford enterprise may well have been more responsible for the rise of 'mass production' . . . unlike Singer, McCormick, and Pope, Ford sought to manufacture the *lowest* priced automobile and to use continuing price reductions to produce even greater demand (p. 5, emphasis in original)

The standardisation of products and process allowed Ford to take the division of labour to new extremes: the automobile was a complex product and yet according to his own account half of the jobs did not require workers with full physical capacity, and 43 per cent of tasks required less than a day of training (Ford & Crowther, 1924, pp. 108–110). It also facilitated the widespread use of special-purpose machine tools and other automation.

The use of the moving assembly line is closely associated with Ford, and has become the symbol of mass production: 'the characteristic labour process of Fordism is *semi-automatic assembly line production*', (Aglietta, 1979, p. 118, emphasis in original). The first experimental line was installed at Ford in 1913, and others were introduced a year later. By that time annual production of the Model T had already reached 300,000 cars, an output similar to single-model plants in the United States today. The moving assembly line was important, but far less so than is often thought. It simply made the division of labour more efficient by increasing the speed of transfer between operatives, but 'The Ford approach was to eliminate labour by machinery, not as the Taylorites customarily did, to take a given production process and improve the efficiency of the workers' (Hounshell, 1985, p.252).

The elimination of labour by machines did not begin with Ford. Over 150 years ago Ure defined the 'philosophy of manufactures' as the 'exposition of general principles, on which productive industry should be conducted by self-acting machines' (1835, p. 9). But the term *automation* was first used to describe the transfer lines at Ford in the late 1940s. The difference between mechanisation during the nineteenth century and automation in the twentieth is not simply one of degree.

In his pioneering study of automation in the United States during the 1950s, Bright (1958) distinguished between the *level* of automation, the *span* across a sequence of activities, and the *extent* of automation of ancillary operations such as machine set-up and maintenance. He concluded that in the mid-1950s automation had reached the level of fixed-sequence program control. Bell (1972) suggests automation of manufacturing takes place along different dimensions: the transformation process itself, including machining and assembly activities; the handling or transfer of materials; and the control of such operations. Moreover it has been argued that automation has occurred in each dimension during successive historical periods (Coombs, 1984; Blackburn *et al.*, 1985): engineers initially concentrated on improving the speed and scale of the transformation processes; this subsequently created bottlenecks in the transfer of materials, and attention focused on such activities, resulting in assembly-line and continuous-flow production during the inter-war years; more recently, as both transformation and transfer have become fully automated, engineers turned to the automation of control.

But there was a price to pay for increasing efficiency through extensive automation. During the 1920s Ford's share of the American automobile market fell from 55 per cent to just 15 per cent, and annual sales of the Model T fell from a peak of almost two million to 800,000:

mass production as Ford had made it and defined it was, for all intents and purposes, dead by 1926. Ford and his production experts had driven mass production into a deep cul-de-sac . . . Automotive consumption in the late 1920s called for a new kind of mass production, a system that could accommodate frequent change and was no longer wedded to the idea of maximum production at minimum cost . . . Ford learned painfully that the times called for a new era, that of 'flexible mass production'. (Hounshell, 1984, pp. 12–13)

In 1927 Ford announced the replacement for the Model T, the Model A. The model changeover required a total plant shutdown; the scrapping of a quarter of the 32,000 machine tools used for the previous model; the refurbishment or rebuilding of half of the existing machine tools; and the purchase of 45,000 new machine tools dedicated to the new model (Hounshell, 1984, pp. 285–8). But mass production did not die with the Model T: by 1929 Ford had built assembly plants in twenty-one countries, and its main rival General Motors was assembling vehicles in sixteen. Mass production only became a truly global phenomenon in the markets of the 1950s. Manufacturers in Europe exploited the high levels of domestic demand and liberalisation of international markets following World War II; and in the United States mass production continued to dominate throughout the 1950s:

if there is any common experience in the operation of these highly automated plants, it is the lack of flexibility . . . The desire to obtain flexibility is a novel or rather uncommon objective of automation . . . Could Ford's 1950 engine plant be adapted to produce a different engine as quickly as its 1940 plant ? Because of much greater investment in equipment, because, perhaps, of the unsuitability of the equipment, it probably would be a slower, more difficult, more expensive job to convert the automated plant. (Bright, 1958, pp. 141–42)

The trend towards more efficient but inflexible production continued to represent manufacturing 'best practice' until the 1980s. Automation was accompanied by a reduction in manufacturing flexibility; a trade-off between efficiency and innovation existed — the so-called 'productivity dilemma' (Abernathy, 1978). Up until the 1970s the increasing rigidity of individual manufacturers and plants was hidden from the consumer by the growing number of manufacturers in the industry and the flexibility of processes downstream. In the automobile industry, body, engine and component manufacture are now highly automated and inflexible, but final assembly has remained labour-intensive and flexible (Schupp, 1988). Advances in manufacturing technology have increased the range of tasks that can be automated; robots have begun to be used for final assembly in automobile plants. But the impact of such developments on flexibility is unclear.

There is a widespread belief that advanced manufacturing technology will overcome the 'productivity dilemma' and is the key to flexible but efficient manufacturing: 'the primary strategic significance of CAM (Computer Aided Manufacturing) lies in its potential for reversing the trend toward more cost-efficient but inflexible productive units (Gerwin, 1982, p. 113); 'compared with the "classical" (electromechanical) automation of mass production, numerically-controlled machine tools, flexible manufacturing systems, robots allow a much greater flexibility of production . . . These have been described as "economies of scope" (Dosi, 1986, p. 20). The premise is that programmable automation is inherently flexible, a view which has quickly become conventional wisdom:

today's computer-based technology reverses this long-term historical trend towards specialised hardware by placing emphasis on specialised software instead. Matching general-purpose machines with special-purpose programming moves the work of production, even in small batches, toward the smooth flow of chemical process operations. (Goldhar & Jelinek, 1983, p. 143)

factory robots and other forms of 'soft automation' have started flexing their muscles, reducing industry's need for capital expenditure sharply. Such flexible machinery is merely reprogrammed — rather than ripped out and replaced — when a factory is being switched over to making a new product. The changeover is completed in hours instead of weeks; the cost of doing so is marginal. (*The Economist*, December 1989)

But do programmable manufacturing technologies such as FMS and robots really represent a radical departure from earlier forms of automation? Numerical control was first demonstrated in 1951, the result of work at the Massachusetts Institute of Technology (MIT) to develop 'a system applicable to machine tools for controlling the position of shafts in accordance with the output of a computing machine' (Ferguson, 1978, p. 78). Nevertheless, the first machines had hard-wired, special-purpose controls, and were highly inflexible. Early NCMT were simply too sophisticated and expensive for most work, and were only suitable for tasks that required high-precision machining at any cost; the original project at MIT was commissioned by the United States Air Force (USAF).

During the 1950s Ferranti in the United Kingdom and Fujitsu Fanuc and Makino Milling in Japan also developed NCMT, but the main technological breakthroughs came in the 1970s: first the use of minicomputer control based on integrated circuit technology, and later microprocessor control based on developments in microelectronics. This made NCMT cheaper,

Table 2.5 Growing importance of microelectronics-based manufacturing technologies worldwide

	1980	1988
Numerically controlled machine tools	65,000*	221,000*
Industrial robots	21,000	260,000
Flexible machining systems (FMS)	70	500

*Figures for US only.
Source: American Machinist, 1989; International Federation of Robotics, 1989; Tchijov & Scheinin, 1989.

more reliable, and more easily programmable; the use of microelectronics roughly halved the cost of the controller, reducing it to around 15-20 per cent of the total machine cost (Jacobsson, 1986, p. 10). As a result many commentators began to talk of a 'microelectronics revolution', and the arrival of the long awaited 'factory of the future' in the guise of computer integrated manufacture (CIM):

the introduction of the inherently flexible minicomputer and microprocessor in the 1970s, combined with common binary logic of numerical controls in different intra-activity automation technologies, provided the opportunity to introduce the first attempts . . . by the 1990s we will surely see the fairly widespread emergence of fully automated production in many sectors including those now characterised by mass production. (Kaplinsky, 1984, p. 106)

Ironically, as the cost of control technology fell, subsequent technological developments focused on other areas of machine tool design. First, tool changing was automated, allowing additional machining operations to be performed on a single machine automatically; next, the handling of workpieces and transfer operations was automated. Consequently the NC milling machine evolved into the machining centre, the NC lathe into the turning centre, and most recently such machines linked to form so-called flexible manufacturing cells and systems. Similarly, the industrial robot began life as a relatively slow hydraulic machine for highly repetitive handling tasks where the main requirement was brute strength. Today most robots are electric and are used for a wide range of tasks where high speed and repeatability are crucial. Programmable machine tools have become increasingly important (Table 2.5), but the emphasis on control technology may be misplaced:

obsession with the novelty and spectacular performance of automatic controls diverts attention from the problems of their application to industry. Although automatic control mechanisms are *necessary* for the achievement of fully automatic factories, they are not *sufficient* in themselves. The full promise of the new technology cannot be realised so long as we think solely in terms of control . . . it is both erroneous and self-limiting to think of the possiblities of automation merely in terms of connecting a computer to today's machines and making precisely the same products in the same way. (Deibold, 1952, pp. 2–32, emphasis in original)

In order to appreciate the impact of flexible automation it is necessary to understand the relationship between products and process, in particular the interaction of markets and manufacturing technology. Technologies do not simply develop according to some 'natural' internal logic ('technology push'), and are not created by market forces ('market pull'). At any time the existing state of technical knowledge will determine the range of opportunities, but changing market requirements will define the precise direction of technological change, and the appropriate cost and performance trade-offs which must be satisfied (Georghiou *et al.*, 1986). This defines what constitutes progress , and focuses the attention of suppliers and users of technologies in certain directions rather than others, along specific technological 'trajectories' (Dosi, 1982, 1988). For example, it has been suggested that the requirements of mass production have influenced the development of industrial robots:

without the existence of factory environments providing an abundance of requirements for such simple motions, it is questionable whether the industrial robot could have been developed at all . . . industrial robots can only find use in areas where, in a very real sense, the human work has already been robotised. (Fleck, 1987b, p. 19)

It is not sufficient to extrapolate current technological trends and assess the impact on existing markets and industries. In particular, manufacturing systems based on technologies such as FMS and robotics do not appear to follow any standard pattern of development or adoption; they can be deployed in a very wide range of ways to match external requirements (Fleck, 1987a). This suggests that the context of use is crucial, and that different companies, sectors, and countries may exhibit distinct patterns: 'values, like economics, permeate technological change. Indeed, sociocultural values, especially their institutional expression, underlie derivation of economic utilities themselves' (Constant, 1980, p. 31). Subsequent chapters explore the implications of this thesis, and attempt to identify current international 'best practice' use of flexible automation.

3

Flexibility and competitiveness

The market and technological trends identified in Chapter 2 suggest that manufacturing flexibility will become increasingly important during the 1990s. This chapter reviews the arguments for greater flexibility in more detail and the various means of achieving this. The role of programmable or so-called 'flexible' manufacturing technologies and flexibility is examined, in particular the significance of microelectronic-based controls and computer-integrated manufacture (CIM).

3.1 Dynamic versus static efficiency

Economies of size and scale are apparent in many activities. At the level of the firm, managerial and financial economies exist, such as improved division of managerial labour and cost reductions in purchases, distribution, and sales. At the level of the plant or factory, technical or scale economies arise through the specialisation of labour and machinery. Clearly the respective 'optimum' size for managerial, financial, and technical economies may differ, resulting in some trade-off (Robinson, 1958). Also, beyond a certain size *diseconomies* of scale may begin to occur, particularly in the case of management control. However, at the factory level such considerations are less important as technical economies tend to dominate:

it often happens that when the scale of output is increased technological considerations are of such overwhelming importance that changes in managerial or transport costs may be of negligible significance. In this case we may neglect them, and plants taking advantage of technological economies will always be able to produce at lower costs than plants that do not, and will be able to dominate the industry. (Penrose, 1968, p. 91)

In practice the 'optimum' scale of plant is such that few industries are

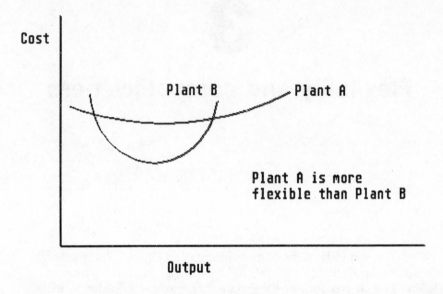

Figure 3.1 Neo-classical concept of flexibility

dominated by a small number of *plants*, although many sectors are dominated by a few major *firms* (Scherer, 1980). This confirms the importance of managerial and financial scale economies. The economists' concept of an efficient firm is one that produces at the minimum point of its long-run average cost curve. The 'optimum firm' will operate at the scale at which existing conditions of organisation and technique produce the lowest average cost, and flexibility is simply interpreted as the flatness of the average cost curve, that is the firm's ability to respond to changes in price/demand (Figure 3.1). This most basic form of the price-elasticity argument can be modified to include price uncertainties, but the effect of more general market uncertainty has largely remained ignored. Within such a narrow framework it is difficult to explain the rationale for multi-product firms or plants. These can only emerge by accident in an economy operating under neo-classical competitive assumptions (Teece, 1980, 1982).

A specialised firm will be most efficient in conditions of constant output, but will be highly vulnerable in an uncertain, rapidly changing market. This is the fundamental advantage capitalism has over other, seemingly more rational alternatives:

> any system, economic or other, that at *every* given point of time fully utilizes its resources to the best advantage may yet in the long run be inferior to a system that does so at *no* given point of time, because the latter's failure to do so may be a condition for the level or speed of long-run performance. (Schumpeter, 1943, p. 83).

Klein (1977) argues that a diversity of firms at the micro-level is necessary for long-term economic growth and stability at the macro-level. Essentially he assumes that static and dynamic efficiency are incompatible at the level of the firm, and therefore an appropriate mix of firm types is necessary to overcome the long-term consequences of Abernathy's 'productivity dilemma'. However, evolutionary theories of the firm argue that all firms must adapt to an ever-changing market environment. Long-term survival no longer depends on 'optimal' behaviour at any point, but on the ability to adapt and learn (Allen, 1988).

In neo-classical economics the firm is associated with a specific product and selects, according to costs, an appropriate mix of inputs and method of manufacture. But in certain cases the cost of joint production of several products is less than the cost of producing each separately, and *economies of scope* are said to exist (Teece, 1980). This may be due to external economies such as supplier or distribution networks, human resources and skills, or where the production technology is sufficiently flexible to manufacture several different products. Therefore the firm possesses specific organisational and technological capabilities and selects appropriate products, or 'critical competences': 'In short, the firm has end products as well as technological choices to confront' (Teece, 1982, p.46).

This also provides a rationale for diversification. In Japan, the direction of diversification is usually determined by the existing technological expertise of the firm. Internal project teams are formed and expertise in the new area is gradually accumulated in-house, rather than through take-over of another firm (Dore, 1986). This is consistent with the maximisation of long-term growth, which is the goal of most Japanese firms, but may conflict with the maximisation of short-term profits (Odagiri, 1989). Thus in the West mergers and acquisitions have traditionally been the favoured methods of diversification (Scherer, 1980; Fallon & Srodes, 1988).

Diversification has often been associated with periods of slow economic growth as a response to market failure and excess capacity:

the Depression apparently triggered the trend towards diversification. Historians point out that the purpose of diversification was not to reduce portfolio risk or to pursue managerial motives, but rather to put slack resources to work. Furthermore, it was the technologically sophisticated firms which led the way. (Teece, 1982, p. 60)

Similarly Piore and Sabel (1984) argue that the trend towards greater flexiblity began as a response to economic 'crisis', but in technologically dynamic firms it has become a strategic weapon. To support their argument they provide a wide range of examples: microprocessors in computing; electric-arc furnaces in steel production; speciality chemicals; and the Pratese textile industry (1984, pp. 194–220). One of the authors has subsequently claimed that American manufacturers have achieved flexible mass production and are now moving towards full 'flexible specialisation' which will allow infinite product variation (Piore, 1987). But such examples of flexible manufacturing are highly selective, and in most cases represent small niche markets rather than a change in international best practice (Ferguson, 1988).

More fundamentally, the whole concept of flexibility used is confused. Examples of technological, product, process, and organisational flexibility are provided, but the relationship between these is unclear. The association between craft practices and flexibility owes more to romantic notions of a bygone era than to any logical necessity or empirical evidence. Similarly the link between flexibility and firm size is tenuous; small may beautiful, but it is not necessarily flexible. Small firms may specialise in a single product, and many large firms manufacture a wide range of products. Clearly a more rigorous concept of flexibility is required.

3.2 Forms of flexibility

Flexibility means all things to all men. It is a relative rather than absolute concept. In the case of batch manufacture Buzacott (1982) emphasises 'the ability of the system to process a wide variety of parts or assemblies without intervention from outside to change the system', whereas in mass production Schonberger (1987) argues that

flexibility is important, therefore, not so much in the production of customised versions of the same product, but in the changeover from one mass-produced product to another . . . manufacturers of appliances, autos, copiers, and cameras, are following the approach of simplifying and focusing product offerings.

In more general terms it is possible to distinguish between two distinct forms of flexibility: *active*, the ability to respond to change by taking appropriate action; and *passive*, the innate ability to function well in more than one state (Mandelbaum, 1978). In the first case the most important consideration is the cost and time required to change, for example to change tooling or provide extra production capacity. In the second, cost and technical factors will determine the capability of a system to deal with a range of possible tasks. The passive flexibility of any system is equivalent to the total number of potential states it can deal with. To specify fully active flexibility three different dimensions must be considered: the range of possible states, the cost of moving from one state to another, and the time taken (Slack, 1983). In some cases it may simply be impossible for a system to operate in certain states, but in others efficiency may be sacrificed (Buzacott, 1982).

A production system with high passive flexibility will be able to accept, that is function in spite of, a wide range of disturbances and can be described as *insensitive*. A system able to change over between different but anticipated tasks, for example to manufacture different product variants, can be described as *versatile*. A system with high active flexibility will also be able to cope with unforeseen changes, for example the introduction of new products, and can be described as *adaptable* (Myrup-Andreasen & Ahm, 1988). In the specific case of FMS a more detailed distinction is possible:

1. *Machine flexibility*: the ease of making the changes required to produce a given set of part/product types;
2. *Process flexibility*: the ability to produce a given set of part/product types in different ways, each possibly using different materials;
3. *Product flexibility*: the ability to change over to produce a new (set of) part(s)/product(s) economically and quickly;
4. *Routing flexibility*: the ability to cope with breakdowns and continue producing a given set of part/product types, e.g. by processing via alternative routes, or every operation can be performed on more than one machine;
5. *Volume flexibility*: the ability to operate a system profitably at different production volumes;
6. *Expansion flexibility*: the capability to expand the system modularly;
7. *Operation flexibility*: the ability to interchange the order of several different operations for each part/product type;
8. *Production flexibility*: the universe of part/product types that the system can produce. (Browne *et al.*, 1984)

In practice conflicts may exist between different types of flexibility, and some form of trade-off may be necessary. A firm must decide which forms of flexibility are most important, and then the most appropriate means of achieving these. This is particularly so in complex systems using sophisticated production technologies. It has been argued that 'the very flexibility of Computer-Aided Manufacturing may introduce some undesirable rigidities to decision making' (Gerwin, 1982, p. 114). In short, computer Integrated Manufacturing (CIM) and flexibility are not synonymous.

3.3 Determinants of flexibility

Numerous factors influence manufacturing flexibility. Most significantly:

The conditions that support a high level of efficiency are entirely different from those that support a high rate of innovation. Decisions that determine equipment development, product-line standardisation, labour-force characteristics, and vertical integration simultaneously influence capabilities for innovation and productivity improvement. (Abernathy, 1978, p. 164)

At the plant level the main factors affecting manufacturing flexibility are work organisation, production planning and control systems, and production technology. At the firm level many other factors will also be important, but these will not be discussed here. The most significant trend in recent years has been towards smaller, more focused factories (Schonberger, 1987; PA Consulting, 1990), and the impact this has had on flexibility.

Work organisation

During the 1980s many firms in the United Kingdom made major efforts to improve the flexibility of labour (ACAS, 1987; IMS, 1984). One report concluded:

we are beginning to witness important changes to orthodox ideas about work organisation and the deployment of labour. As yet such changes cannot be said to add up to new and coherent employment strategies on the part of the employers. But what is unmistakable is a managerial imperative to secure more flexibility from the labour force, and a readiness to exploit new ways of achieving it. (Atkinson, 1984, pp. 1–2)

Several factors contributed to this trend: technology; skill specificity and training costs; labour shortage; institutional pressures; and national training provisions (Atkinson, 1984, pp. 6–7), but 'the immediate catalyst to this new attitude has been a combination of technological change and recession' (Wickens, 1987, p. 41). On the one hand, technological developments question the historical boundaries between trades or crafts, and, on the other, increased market uncertainty requires workers to respond more readily to changes in demand. Three distinct types of labour flexibility can be identified:

1. *Functional*: the ease with which the tasks performed by workers can be adjusted to meeting changes in technology, markets, or company policy;
2. *Numerical*: the ease with which the number of workers can be adjusted to meet fluctuations in demand;
3. *Financial*: the extent to which the structure of pay encourages and supports the numerical and functional flexibility; (Atkinson, 1985, p. 26)

Functional flexibility includes: *core skill*, whereby the normal trade or craft remains, but an appreciation of other skills is required; *dual skill*, again the core skill remains, but the worker must also become proficient at a second discipline, for example a maintenance electrician undergoing training in hydraulic systems in order to service robots; and *multi-skill*, where a larger number of skills are required (Connock, 1985). Numerical and financial flexibility can be achieved through alternative types of employment contract, such as annual hours, minimum/maximum hours, and various forms of job-sharing, part-time and home-working arrangements. Atkinson (1985) proposes a general model which consists of a permanent core group of functionally flexible workers supplemented by various peripheral groups which may or may not be employees of the firm, including, for example, sub-contractors, seasonal, and home workers.

In practice relatively few employers in the United Kingdom have yet explicitly reorganised their labour force on such a basis, and manpower policy appears still to be largely dictated by pragmatism and opportunism. In particular, firms have exploited the shift in the balance of power in industrial relations since the early 1980s. There has been a marked increase in numerical labour flexibility in recent years, particularly the use of temporary workers (Atkinson & Meager, 1986). At the same time firms in Japan have been reducing their reliance on numerical flexibility, such that temporary workers now account for between five and six per cent of the total work-force in both the UK and Japan (Dore, 1986; King, 1988).

It is much more difficult to estimate any change in functional labour flexibility. Case studies suggest that functional flexibility is more common-place in capital-intensive plants, whereas numerical and financial flexibility are more important in labour-intensive processes (Atkinson, 1984). Japanese 'trans-plants' in the United Kingdom were among the first to require functional flexibility from their workers. The first formal agreement in the United Kingdom was between Toshiba and the electricians' union, the EETPU, which stated:

the trade union recognises and supports the complete flexibility of jobs and duties within the company, both within departments and between the various departments of the company, subject to individual skills and capabilities. In return the company recognises and accepts the need for training and retraining in the broadening of skills and in new technological developments. (Wickens, 1987, p. 46)

More recently, the agreement between Nissan (UK) and the engineering union AEU specified that:

(a) To ensure the fullest use of facilities and manpower, there will be complete flexibility and mobility of employees;
(b) It is agreed that changes in technology, processes and practices will be introduced and that such changes will affect both productivity and manning levels;
(c) To ensure such flexibility and change, employees will undertake and/or undertake training for all work as required by the Company. All employees will train other employees as required. (*ibid.*, pp. 43-4).

There are now more than sixty Japanese manufacturing plants operating in the United Kingdom, and most have negotiated similar flexibility deals. Thus in both functional and numerical terms there is evidence that manufacturers in the United Kingdom are moving towards 'Japanese' levels of labour flexibility. However, it is important not to overstate the similarities between Japanese working practices and such trends as significant differences do exist. A study of British manufacturers concluded that 'many firms appear to be simply taking advantage of a depressed labour market and implementing some aspects of the [Japanese] model opportunistically without any long term strategy' (Atkinson, 1984, pp. 19–20). Other studies suggest that many British firms are unwilling to make the commitment to training that flexibility demands (McCormick, 1986; Senker, 1988).

Production planning and control

Three basic types of plant configuration or layout exist:

1. Product, line or flow, where the sequence of operations is dictated by the requirements of a specific product or family of similar products, e.g., the classic assembly line or chemical plant;
2. Process or functional, where all facilities performing the same function are grouped together in specialised shops or departments, e.g., the jobbing shop;
3. Group technology, where families of similar parts or products are processed in groups of machines laid out exclusively for performing most, if not all, of the required operations on those parts or products.

Wherever possible manufacturers will choose the line or flow configuration as control of production is easier and material flow is maximised. In most other cases the functional configuration is used as this allows high machine utilisation. Group technology has not been widely adopted, despite demonstrating considerable benefits over the functional layout. This is probably because of the considerable effort required to identify family characteristics and adapt work organisation and design plant layout in order to exploit these (Burbridge, 1978).

Graphical design techniques allow the optimisation of a single variable, but are unable to deal with multiple and possibly conflicting criteria such as handling costs, capital costs, operating costs, machine utilisation, flexibility, and line balancing. Similarly, existing mathematical models for the optimisation of plant layout are unsatisfactory and involve subjective evaluation of alternative criteria.

Three of the most problematic areas of production management are capacity planning, production planning and control, and inventory planning and control. Capacity planning is essentially a medium- to long-term problem, whereas production and inventory planning and management are operational considerations. Decisions regarding capacity will primarily affect the passive flexibility of a production system whereas systems of control will determine the active flexibility of the system, or the ability to change. Traditionally in capital-intensive mass production high machine utilisation is important, and therefore accurate forecasting of demand and capacity planning are necessary. The production process is relatively well-defined, and consequently production control is almost routine. In contrast, accurate production planning is impossible in small batch production, and production control is difficult but critical (Wild, 1985).

Mathematical approaches to such problems exist, including statistical queueing theory, critical path and network analysis, and linear programming techniques (Dale & Michelon, 1986), but in practice these are of limited value:

the very generality of these problems, however, must limit the value of the mathematical methods developed for their solution, if only because of the fact that such methods normally consider the optimisation of a single criteria . . . it is for this reason that such methods have proved to be of limited value in the design of production systems . . . consequently important problems such as assembly line balancing are generally tackled by heuristic methods, and (increasingly) with the assistance of computer simulation. (Wild, 1985, pp. 108–10)

But by definition heuristic procedures are based on 'simple rules or procedures which if applied consistently *have been found to provide satisfactorily good* but not necessarily optimum results' (*ibid.*, p.59, emphasis in original). Heuristic procedures form the basis of models for computer simulation and so-called 'expert systems' for production management. In such cases there is a real danger that simple rules of thumb based on past experience will be given spurious precision, resulting in pseudo-scientific management: 'the essence of the machine is its software, but the essence of the software is its philosophy' (Roszak, 1986, p. 81).

In scheduling, for example, time and capacity are the two main constraints to be considered, the two extremes being where either infinite capacity is assumed and scheduling determined by delivery dates, or delivery dates are ignored and scheduling determined by capacity. Materials control is either based on signals generated by sales — order point generation — or signals from stock — stock point generation (Lockyer, 1983). The former is typical of custom or batch production, and the latter of mass production. Real production systems will of course use a blend of such systems, but order point material control is the 'ideal' in all cases although due to the sheer volume of data to be handled is in practice less common than various forms of stock point control. In principle computer systems such as material requirements planning (MRP) and manufacturing resource planning (MRP II) are designed to deal with such problems, but in practice the schedules generated by such programmes often do not relate to reality on the shop floor:

The main practical criticism of MRP II, then, is that it doesn't work, or at least has not been proved to work so far. The main theorectical criticism is that it rests on an idea of planning the capacity of a factory which, the critics contend, is fundamentally flawed. (*The Engineer*, 16 November 1989)

As is now well known, Japanese manufacturers have overcome some of the problems of production planning and control by adopting a different manufacturing philosophy to that of their counterparts in the West. In the late 1950s Ono Taiichi of Toyota rejected current 'best practice' production management, and reversed the conventional direction of materials and information flow: rather than 'push' materials and components through the system, they were 'pulled' from final assembly; sub-assemblies and components arrived at successive stages of production 'just in time'. Consequently expensive buffer stocks were eliminated and other inventory reduced (Cusumano, 1985). The traditional function of buffer stocks is to reduce uncertainty:

1. Stocks of materials and purchased components reduce the risk of delivery delays or problems at suppliers premises, and allow bulk discounts;
2. Work in progress decouples different stages of production so that isolated disturbances such as machine breakdown do not affect the entire system;
3. Stocks of finished goods act as a buffer against fluctuations in demand. (Wild, 1985)

In his excellent account of Japanese manufacturing techniques, Schonberger argues that the Japanese 'do not cast off Western principles but do change the emphasis: To put it simply, the Western emphasis is on good balance, whereas the Japanese place as much or more emphasis on flexibility' (1982, p. 132). By eliminating buffer stocks, just-in-time system (JIT) production control exposes any inadequacies in the process, and therefore demands high quality components, reliable machines, rapid machine changeovers, and frequent and reliable delivery of components and raw materials: JIT simply cannot be implemented in isolation.

By matching material and information flows and thus simplifying scheduling JIT can also improve flexibility. In automobile manufacture, for example, mixed-model scheduling is simplified as orders orginate from final assembly, and appropriate sub-assemblies and components are 'pulled' through the production system (Schonberger, 1982). It has also been estimated that the use of the JIT allows Toyota to accommodate variations in monthly demand of up to 30 per cent (Cusumano, 1985). In conventional push-type production systems any forecasting errors are amplified at each stage of manufacture up to final production; in pull-type systems no such amplification occurs, minimising the effect of any forecasting errors (Muramatsu *et al.*, 1985).

Production technology

As noted in the previous chapter, there is a widespread belief that programmable automation such as FMS and industrial robots are the key to flexible, but efficient manufacturing:

the efficiency in production results from adapting the equipment to the task at hand: the specialisation of the equipment to the operation. With conventional technology, this adaptation is done by physical adjustments in the equipment; whenever the product is changed, the specialised machine is rebuilt . . . with computer technology, the equipment (the hardware) is adapted to the operation by the computer program (the software); therefore the equipment can be put to new uses without physical adjustments — simply by reprogramming. (Piore & Sabel, 1984, p. 260)

In short, it is assumed that programmability is equivalent to flexibility. However, this preoccupation with control technology and the emphasis on software may be inappropriate. In FMS, for example, flexibility is largely determined by the numerous hardware components — type of machine tool, materials handling system, in-process storage arrangements — as well as the control system. For materials handling alone numerous options exist, such as different types of conveyor, gantry cranes, robots, or automatic guided vehicles (AGVs) (Bessant & Haywood, 1985). In many cases the software is the most complex part of the system, and is not easily changed. Future reprogramming requirements must be anticipated when the system is designed. In short, the required level of passive flexibility must be determined before the software is developed, and the active flexibility of most FMS appears to be limited:

flexibility has always been available in the batch machine shop, but the price to be paid [for it] has usually been prohibitive. It is, however, important to realise that a flexible machining system is a compromise between the infinite component flexibility and low efficiency of a general-purpose machine shop and the high efficiency and inflexibility of a transfer machine. The price to to be paid for the advantages is the acceptance of limited flexibility. (NEDC, 1984, p. 16)

Hardware configuration is equally important in robotics, and software is often secondary. Industrial robots consist of: a basic mechanical structure and configuration; actuators or drive system; end-effector, tool, or gripper; control system and programming language; and perhaps sensors. In addition, a system will include many of the components found in FMS: fixtures, tool changers, materials handling devices, etc. Dunlop (1983) identifies ten components of robot flexibility, based on a narrow definition of flexibility: 'the span of task variety which a manipulator, or system of manipulators, can encompass' (Table 3.1).

This model is derived from a conceptual framework proposed by Hiroshi Makino, inventor of the SCARA robot (Chapter 7). However, Dunlop

Table 3.1 Ten dimensions of robot flexibility

Intrinsic elements of DEXTERITY:	SPATIAL MOVEMENT
	DEGREES OF FREEDOM
	GRASP
	COMPLIANCE
Intrinsic elements of PRODUCTIVITY:	SPEED OF MOVEMENT
	POWER
	ROBUSTNESS
Intrinsic elements of PROGRAMMABILITY:	SENSORY FEEDBACK
	LANGUAGE
	PROGRAMME

Source: Dunlop, 1983, p. 20.

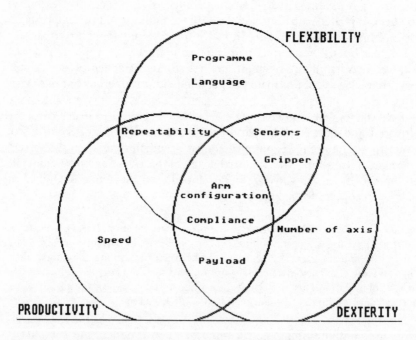

Figure 3.2 Importance of various aspects of robot design

substitutes 'programmability' for 'flexibility' in Makino's original model (Figure 3.2), arguing that 'flexibility appears to be a concept from the same anti-positive paradigm as ideas of evolution and relativity, a world without firm laws or best answers, full of constantly changing trade-offs' (1983, p.23). But flexibility is important precisely because the real world is full of constantly changing trade-offs!

Whether or not a robot makes use of sensory information is often used to distinguish between so-called 'first-' and 'second-' generation machines.

The main drawback of first generation machines is that they cannot obtain information concerning their work environment and therefore require well-structured environments involving expensive and inflexible fixtures and parts-orientation devices; in addition they must also be programmed on-line, i.e., taught a particular sequence of movements on the shop floor.

As a result, product-specific fixtures, grippers, and parts-feeders may account for between a half and two-thirds of the total cost of a first-generation system. Second-generation robots are more expensive, but in principle at least, the cost of such fixtures should be significantly reduced, and they promise the ability to be programmed off-line, allowing better computer integration. However, serious technical obstacles still exist:

(a) Sensors are still relatively expensive and require considerable computational power to translate signals into appropriate action;
(b) Information from sensors cannot readily be fed into robot or process control systems;
(c) There is still no single interface standard. Compliance with Manufacturing Automation Protocol (MAP) is still the exception rather than the rule, and in any case MAP does not deal with software compatibility;
(d) On-line programming languages are still used extensively, but are unsuitable for CIM;
(e) Current off-line languages cannot exploit CAD databases in real-time, and are unable to incorporate sensor input or the effect of tool compliance;
(f) The absolute positional accuracy of existing robots still results in deviations between the geometric model used off-line and actual conditions on the shop floor.

Consequently, existing sensor-based, second-generation robotic applications are expensive and application-specific, rather than cheaper and more flexible than their first-generation counterparts. For example, the use of machine vision usually requires the use of special light sources, high optical-contrast between parts and environment, accurate positioning of cameras and parts, and dedicated programming. Flexibility is sacrificed to ensure system robustness and reliability. Thus a recent review of developments in robotics concluded:

It has often been stated that the greatest virtue of robots lies in their flexibility. The implication is that a manufacturer might best utilize a robot by assuming it to perform a variety of tasks. In fact this almost never occurs. The cost of preparing a robot to perform a single task is very high and is usually not justified unless the robot is to be dedicated to that task. The primary advantage of flexibility brought about by programmability of a robot is that it can be reprogrammed to accommodate small changes in the task to which it has been assigned. (Seering, 1987, pp. 28–9)

3.4 Towards evaluation

The evaluation of flexibility is complicated by the fact that unlike other manufacturing objectives such as productivity and quality, it is essentially a measure of the *potential* of a system. Therefore optimisation is simply impossible:

the basic principle of optimality suggests that when we are in a particular state at any time we should do the best possible from then on without regard to how we reached this state . . . We must not allow our greed for apparent optimality in the present to close off all our good alternatives in the future, and leave us in such a bad state that the best we can do is very poor indeed. (Mandelbaum, 1978, p. 19)

The first step towards evaluating the flexibility of a system is to assess the types of flexibility which are likely to be most important, for example, the ability to offer a wide range of product variants or the ability to operate profitably over a wide range of output. The next step is to audit the capability of the system to deliver such flexibility (Mandelbaum, 1978; Slack, 1983). The capability of any system can be assessed by examining inputs and outputs.

On the input side, it is normally possible to separate product-specific costs from those which are more general, and the balance between 'flexible' and 'dedicated' equipment can be estimated (Lim, 1986). On the output side, proxy measures of flexibility include the number of product variants manufactured and product life cycles. Both approaches have their limitations. The former tends to rely on arbitrary scales of flexibility, and there is the danger that the sophistication of production technology will be confused with flexibility (Browne *et al.*, 1984). The latter approach can only provide a 'snapshot' of existing practice, and the dimension of time is lost: 'the key difference between complexity and flexibility is that complexity is the product/part variation at a given point in time; flexibility on the other hand is the ability to dynamically shift product/part mixes over time' (Krafcik, 1988a, p. 3).

Recently there have been many attempts to quantify flexibility. In one scheme, several different types of flexibility are converted into non-dimensional indices, and allocated to the axes of a Cartesian co-ordinate system to form a Flexibility Evaluation Vector (Ito, 1987). In this way up to three different types of flexibility can be represented by the magnitude and directional cosine of their resultant vector, allowing structural and functional characteristics of different systems to be compared (Figure 3.3). Although designed for the evaluation of FMS, the concept of a flexibility vector can be applied in more general terms (Mandelbaum, 1978). For

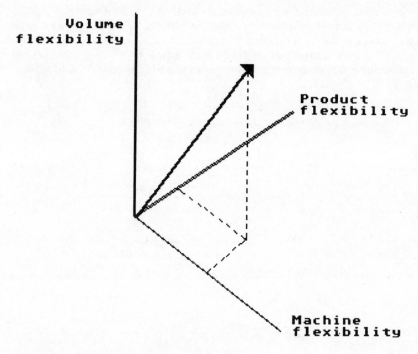

Figure 3.3 Flexibility evaluation vector
Source: Ito, 1987

example, the three dimensions of active flexibility — number of potential states, cost of changing state, and time taken — could usefully be represented this way.

But flexibility is relative. Therefore it is necessary to compare existing flexibility with past performance and that of current competitors. Any assessment must take into account the flexibility of previous systems and technology, and the flexibility demanded by the market. Obviously a plant where welding robots have replaced workers has probably become less flexible, but one where robots have replaced dedicated multi-welding machines has improved its flexibility. Similarly the flexibility required in the capital goods industry is clearly different to that demanded in the consumer goods sector, and it would be meaningless to compare the two.

Trends in markets, organisation of production, and manufacturing technology suggest that the greatest changes in flexibility are taking place in mass production. Product variety is increasing, and life cycles are becoming shorter. The most significant developments in work organisation and production planning and control have come from Japanese manufacturers of consumer durables. The limited flexibility of technologies such as FMS and robotics also appears to be most appropriate for high volume, high variety production. A recent survey revealed that:

A large number of Japanese manufacturers are banking on aggressive deployment of technology to achieve economic flexibility in manufacturing. They seem to be focused on as a group on developing 'breakthrough' capabilities that fundamentally change the way manufacturing is done. They appear to be developing flexible process technologies which will yield both low costs and flexibility. (Ferdows *et al.*, 1986, p. 14).

4

Global trends in flexible automation

Most commentators have concentrated on the potential benefits of programmable automation for small, batch manufacturers. Yet recent market and organisational developments suggest that the most significant improvements in flexibility are likely to occur in mass production. This chapter identifies patterns of adoption and assesses the impact of three key manufacturing technologies: numerically controlled machine tools (NCMT), flexible machining systems (FMS), and industrial robots.

4.1 Numerically controlled machine tools

Numerical control has been defined as

the dimensional and sequential operation of a machine tool by means of coded numeric information . . . to cause, at the appropriate time, the movement of the parts or parts being machined and for the tools involved together with, in some cases, selection of current speeds, feed rates, etc. (Ferguson, 1978, p. 89)

It is possible to distinguish between computer numerical control (CNC), where each machine tool or group of machine tools has its own controller, and direct numerical control (DNC), where a central computer replaces the input devices of a group of machines and may also deal with work loads and sequencing. Numerical control is often associated with the application of microelectronics, but NCMT were developed much earlier. The concept of negative feedback, or cybernetic control, was developed during World War II to control heavy artillery, and high-performance hydraulic and electroservo mechanisms were developed for this purpose.

In 1949 the Massachusetts Institute of Technology (MIT) undertook a project for the 'development of a system applicable to machine tools for controlling the position of shafts in accordance with the output of a computing machine' (Ferguson, 1978, p. 89). Although the original specification included *computer* control, the first NCMT demonstrated in 1951 had hard-wired electronic controls. The project was supported by the US Air Force, and the USAF bought the first 100 NCMT in the late 1950s after the civil aircraft manufacturers refused to invest in the technology. Few manufacturers outside the defence industry were prepared to pay such a high price for increased precision. Nevertheless several firms overseas also developed NCMT during the 1950s: in 1956 Ferranti delivered the first NCMT to British industry, and two years later Fujitsu Fanuc, in conjunction with the Makino Milling Machine Company, produced the first NCMT in Japan.

The Japanese licensed much of the original technology from the United States, but in 1976 made their most significant contribution to the development of NCMT through the application of microelectronic controls, four years earlier than their competitors in the United States (US Congress, 1990, p. 156). This roughly halved the cost of the controller, reducing it to just 15–20 per cent of the total cost of an NCMT (Jacobsson, 1986, p. 10). Cheaper and more reliable control systems were a necessary but not sufficient condition for the widespread adoption of NCMT. Even after the introduction of microelectronic controls NCMT manufacturers in the United States and Europe continued to focus on the needs of large, sophisticated users. In contrast, Japanese machine tool builders began to pursue what has been described as an 'overall cost leadership strategy' (Jacobsson, 1986, p. 10). Led by Fanuc, which had split from its parent Fujitsu in 1972, Japanese suppliers concentrated on producing standardised, lower-performance, and thus significantly cheaper NCMT suitable for a wider range of users:

instead of using general-purpose equipment to produce special-purpose machines, they are doing the reverse — using special-purpose equipment to produce general-purpose machines to fill the craft needs of the rest of the metalworking sector. (Piore & Sabel, 1984, p. 219).

Japanese NCMT are generally simpler and cheaper than those produced elsewhere. They use lower-powered motors, and therefore can be made lighter than more powerful machines which need to be heavy to maintain rigidity and damp vibrations. For example, Japanese numerically controlled lathes, the most common form of NCMT, are typically half the weight and a third of the cost of machines produced in Europe and the United States (Jacobsson, 1986). Consequently Japanese suppliers quickly came to dominate world markets: their share of world production grew from 15 per cent by value, and 30 per cent in terms of numbers in 1975, to 54 per cent and 72 per cent respectively by 1984 (Jacobsson, 1986); and two-thirds of NCMT sold in the United States in 1989 were made in Japan (US Congress, 1990, p. 156). But although exports of NCMTs from Japan have

Table 4.1 Share of production of NCMT of six OECD countries (in monetary terms) (%)

	1975	1980	1983
Japan	23.1	54.2	54.4
US	43.8	21.8	16.5
FRG	11.5	11.7	16.5
Italy	8.5	6.6	6.2
UK	7.8	3.0	3.7
France	5.3	2.7	2.7
Total	100.0	100.0	100.0

Source: ECE, 1986.

grown dramatically, the domestic market continues to account for the majority of sales (Japan Economic Almanac, 1985).

By the mid-1980s NCMT represented around three-quarters of all machine tool production and about two-thirds of all new machine tool investment, leading a recent report to conclude that 'the rapid diffusion of NCMTs began at the end of the 1970s. Today it is extensive' (Edquist & Jacobsson, 1988, p. 25). But despite this impressive growth in production and investment in NCMT, the impact of the technology has been limited. In the United Kingdom NCMT accounted for just 6.7 per cent of all machine tools in use in 1987 (Metalworking Production, 1988); in the United States the proportion was 9.5 per cent (American Machinist, 1989); and even in Japan only 11.3 per cent of all machine tools are numerically controlled (MITI, 1988).

There are two main reasons for this. Firstly, numerical control is still most commonly applied to metal-cutting rather than metal-forming machine tools, and in particular to turning (lathes). This is because numerical control offers no significant advantage when applied to the inherently inflexible hardware common in metal-forming. Thus over a third of all NCMT in use are lathes, whereas lathes account for less than a fifth of all machine tools in use (Jacobsson, 1986; Metalworking Production, 1988). Secondly, NCMT are only economic in specific circumstances, in which sufficient throughput is possible or a certain level of precision is necessary (Hunt & Hunt, 1983). This is reflected in the sectoral and size distribution of user firms. Not surprisingly there is a high correlation between the share of total stock of NCMT, and the share of the number of hours worked by metal-cutting operatives in different industries:

the pattern of diffusion of NCMTs can to a very large extent be explained by the nature of the industrial process at branch level . . . [but] since the coefficients are not closer to 1, other factors explaining the choice between conventional machine tools and NCMTs at the branch level must also exist. (Edquist & Jacobsson, 1988, p. 31)

Table 4.2 Impact of NCMT by sector in the UK, US and Japan

Sector	% of machine tools in industry NC		
	UK	US*	Japan
Metal goods	4.3	5.6	9.2
Mechanical engineering	7.4	10.5	12.2
Electrical engineering	6.9	7.1	13.5
Motor vehicle and parts	6.4	12.8	9.8
Aerospace	11.6		n.a.
Precision instruments	7.9	12.0	8.4
All industry	6.7	9.5	11.3

*Data for US relates to 1988; UK and Japan is for 1987.
Source: Metalworking Production, 1988; American Machinist, 1989; MITI, 1988.

The greatest impact of NCMT has been in those sectors characterised by high-precision, batch machining. In most countries the penetration of NCMT has been most significant in the aerospace industry (Table 4.2). In addition, in many cases the defence industry is a major user of such technology. The US Department of Defense directly owns a significant proportion of machine tools, and it was estimated that together with the civil aircraft industry it accounted for around 5 per cent of all machine tools in use in 1983 (American Machinist, 1983). A more recent survey found that 58 per cent of establishments making military products used NCMT, but only 36 per cent of other establishments (US Congress, 1990, p. 155). This tends to support the argument that the requirements of such special customers has influenced the development of the technology in the United States (Jacobsson, 1986; Noble, 1979).

Nevertheless, the availability of cheaper, less sophisticated NCMT from Japan has had a significant impact in smaller firms. In the United States smaller plants have made large investments in NCMT in recent years, and as a result appear to have improved their competitiveness (Acs *et al.*, 1988; American Machinist, 1989). Similarly, in the United Kingdom 78 per cent of the NCMT used by subcontractors were installed between 1982 and 1987, increasing their share of all NCMTs in use from 14 per cent to 23 per cent respectively; over the same period the automobile industry's use of dedicated transfer lines has remained constant, representing 3.6 per cent of all machine tools used in that sector (Metalworking Production, 1983, 1988). This suggests that NCMTs have tended to replace conventional machine tools rather than transfer lines. In short, there has been little improvement in flexibility.

A single NCMT typically replaces between three and six conventional machine tools in terms of throughput, but costs only three to four times as much (Jacobsson, 1986; Metalworking Production, 1983). A NCMT is programmable, but is not as flexible as the conventional machines it

Table 4.3 Investment in NCMTs in large and small plants in Japan, 1970–1981 (million yen)

Year	Large Plants (>300 emp.)	Density*	Small plants (<300 emp.)	Density*
1970	15,510	4.7	7,404	0.8
1972	13,951	4.2	10,600	1.1
1974	25,310	7.6	25,547	2.7
1976	17,069	5.2	22,178	2.3
1978	19,957	6.0	38,445	4.0
1980	68,847	20.0	126,960	13.3
1981	92,068	27.8	153,292	16.0

Source: Jacobson, 1986; Statistics Bureau, Japan, 1985.
*Investment in NCMT (¥m.) per thousand employees based on 1981 labour statistics.

replaces. Therefore NCMT are unsuitable for most 'job shop' and small batch production unless high-precision machining is required. But alternatively NCMT can replace special-purpose machines such as transfer lines, thus improving flexibility. This appears to be the case in Japan.

It has been argued that the absence of a significant military or aerospace sector in Japan was the reason that suppliers there developed cheaper, less sophisticated machines than their counterparts in the United States; that instead Japanese manufacturers of NCMT concentrated on the needs of the huge number of small, domestic sub-contracting firms (Jacobsson, 1986). It is true that small firms in Japan have invested in NCMT more than larger firms since the introduction of cheaper machines in the late 1970s. But in terms of investment in NCMT per employee larger plants were still the major users of the technology in 1981 (Table 4.3).

Large firms in Japan are clearly making significant investment in NCMT, and it appears that in many cases NCMT are replacing special-purpose machine tools rather than conventional machine tools. For example, four basic types of lathe exist, each requiring a different trade-off between flexibility and efficiency: the conventional or engine lathe which is the most flexible but least efficient; the numerically controlled lathe; the revolver lathe; and the fully automatic lathe (Jacobsson, 1986). In Japan NCMT mainly replaced conventional engine lathes up until the early 1980s, but since then have also replaced automatic lathes (Table 4.4).

In short, no single pattern of development and adoption of NCMT exists. Rather, NCMT appear to 'have different consequences and be used to different ends according to prevailing traditions . . . [including] technical, organisational, and labour' (Sorge *et al.*, 1983, p. 39). In the United Kingdom and United States suppliers have concentrated on expensive, sophisticated machines suitable for the aerospace and defence industry; cheaper, less sophisticated machines imported from Japan have had the

Table 4.4 Proportion of annual investment in various types of lathe in Japan, 1973–1983

	Engine	CNC	Automatic
1973	31.4	22.7	33.6
1975	37.7	23.2	26.1
1977	15.1	42.9	36.0
1979	17.3	51.8	28.0
1981	n.a.	45.0	n.a.
1983	11.7	69.2	15.4

Source: Jacobsson, 1986.

greatest impact in smaller companies. There is little evidence of any improvement in flexibility in either case. However, in Japan NCMT have in many cases also replaced special-purpose machines in larger plants, thereby increasing flexibility.

4.2 Flexible machining systems

The automation of tool changing allowed additional machining operations to be performed automatically on a single NCMT: the NC milling machine evolved into the machining centre; the NC lathe into the turning centre. More recently, the automation of workpiece handling and transfer allowed groups of machining and milling centres to be linked to form so-called flexible manufacturing cells and systems. No generally accepted definition of a flexible machining or manufacturing system (FMS) exists, and consequently the technology has become 'all things to all men' (Bessant & Haywood, 1985). FMS has clearly captured the imagination of many, and is largely responsible for the resurrection of that phantom of the 1950s — the 'factory of the future':

the introduction of the inherently flexible minicomputer and microprocessor in the 1970s, combined with the common binary logic of numerical controls in different intra-activity automation technologies, provided the opportunity to introduce the first attempts at intra-sphere automation. First came the machine centre . . . the final major development, in embryonic form in the early 1980s, was the flexible manufacturing system . . . by the 1990s we will surely see the fairly widespread emergence of fully automated production in many sectors including those now characterised by small batch prodution. (Kaplinsky, 1984)

The first FMS was probably 'System 24' developed by Williamson in the United Kingdom for the Molins company in 1962, although it was simply described as a 'machining complex' at the time. Like two contemporary systems developed by the American firms Cincinnati-Milacron and White-Sundstrand, 'System 24' was essentially a collection of single-purpose NCMT linked by conveyor so that palletised work pieces could be automatically transferred between machines (Ferguson, 1978; Jablonoski, 1985). But as with stand-alone NCMTs, these early systems were not commercially successful due to their high cost, complexity, and poor reliability. More practical systems followed the application of microelectronic controls in the early 1980s.

However, due to the complexity of FMS, few companies could offer complete 'turn-key' systems. Instead most suppliers concentrated on specific mechanical, electronic, and software components of FMS: machine-tool builders. electronic manufacturers, and computer firms all contributed to the development of FMS during the 1980s. Machine tools and handling equipment typically account for 80 per cent of total systems costs, and therefore machine-tool builders continue to dominate the market. In the United States the main suppliers of FMS are Cincinnati Milacron, Kearney & Trecker, Ingersoll, White-Sundstrand, and Ex-Cell-O. Fanuc, Hitachi Seiki, Makino Milling, Mitsubishi Heavy Industries, Toshiba Machine, Toyoda, and Yamazaki are the largest suppliers of FMS in Japan. Similarly in Europe, German machine-tool builders continue to dominate, but subsidiaries of automotive firms are becoming increasingly important (ECE, 1986). This is indicative of the growing role of users in the development of FMS: 'in almost all instances in Sweden systems installed at this time have been jointly developed by hardware companies, software suppliers, government institutions, and considered most important, *the users of the systems*' (Haywood & Bessant, 1987, p. 38, emphasis in original). As a result Bessant concludes that:

various forms of joint venture or alliance between different actors on the supply side are emerging to meet this need. In addition to closer integration among actors on the supply side of the automation market there is a need for closer interaction with users in the configuration, development, implementation and long term support. (1988, p. 370).

Problems of definition, together with the systemic nature of FMS, limit the usefulness of traditional machine-tool statistics, and make accurate estimates of total installations and international comparisons difficult. On the basis of various national surveys there were estimated to be of the order of several tens of thousands of FMU, several thousand FMC, and less than 300 FMS in use worldwide in 1985 (ECE, 1986). Japan clearly took an early lead in the application of FMS, and by 1987 there were estimated to be over 250 systems in use (MITI, 1988), suggesting there were only around 500 full FMS in use worldwide (Table 4.5).

Compared with stand-alone NCMTs the adoption of FMS has been slow. This is probably due to the relative high cost and immaturity of the

Table 4.5 Number of FMS worldwide, 1980–1987

	Number of installations		
	1980	1985	1987
FRG	10	35	74[a]
Italy	n.a.	25	n.a.
France	2	17	48
Sweden	8	11	20[b]
United Kingdom	3	9	n.a.
Other Western European	2	25	n.a.
Subtotal	25	122	n.a.
Japan	28	100	254
United States	15	47	81
Total	68	269	>500[c]

[a]Figure for 1986.
[b]Estimate from Haywood & Bessant, 1987b.
[c]Author's estimate.
Source: Bessant & Haywood, 1985; ECE, 1986; MITI, 1988; NEDC, 1984; Tchijov & Sheinin, 1989.

technology. No FMS is 'typical', but experience indicates that such systems normally cost in excess of £1 million, and surveys of existing systems in the United Kingdom and United States suggest an average cost of between £5 million and £7.5 million (Bessant & Haywood, 1985; Ingersoll Engineers, 1984). A significant proportion of such costs are due to product-specific components such as pallets, tooling, and fixtures. In one case 1,600 dedicated fixtures were needed to produce 400 different components (ECE, 1986). More fundamentally, technological limitations still exist. Most FMS are based on machining (milling) centres, and are therefore confined to the machining of prismatic parts, such as engines and gears; more recently FMS based on turning centres have been developed, but few commercial systems can handle both prismatic and rotational parts.

As a result the diffusion of FMS has been very limited. Technical considerations have restricted application to those sectors in which the machining of prismatic parts such as gears, transmissions, and engines is important. Financial considerations have confined FMS to larger, high-volume plants. FMS has had little impact in the electrical or electronics sectors (Table 4.6). It is more difficult to assess the impact of flexible machining cells from published statistics, but case studies suggest that these are becoming increasingly common in smaller plants (Bessant & Haywood, 1985; Haywood & Bessant, 1987a).

Users of FMS claim significant benefits, but it is unclear to what extent these are the result of the technology. According to one study, 'on average

Table 4.6 Distribution of FMS by industrial sector & country

	% of total installations in each country					
	US	Japan	FRG	France	UK	Italy
Automobiles	7	6	26	18	15	22
Aerospace	21	0	9	10	3	3
Agricultural machinery	31	10	0	15	11	22
Machine tools	16	33	22	3	17	19
Engines	14	26	22	8	28	19
Electrical	5	7	13	10	6	6
Electronics	0	3	0	8	2	3
Total	100	100	100	100	100	100

Source: Arcangeli *et al.,* 1987; Edquist & Jacobsson, 1988; NEDC, 1984.

40% of the benefits predicted for an FMS are in fact achievable or have been achieved before the FMS is delivered' (Dempsey, 1983), and another claimed that 'approximately half of the benefits of FMS were derived from managerial and work based organisational changes . . . the non-FMS company . . . had achieved a 60% reduction in stocks held and a 30% increase in output just by adopting "good management and methodological practices" (Bessant & Haywood, 1985, p. 27). However, flexibility is arguably the *raison d'être* of FMS, and it is on this basis success must be judged.

By this criterion FMS has not proved to be an unqualified success, contrary to the rhetoric of its proponents. A study of installations in the United States discovered that

in most cases systems were relatively inflexible. Thus part numbers were restricted to an average of eight; of all the components manufactured in the plant within a given size envelope only 3–4% could be produced on the FMS; and in the event of the product failing a high proportion of the FMS would become obsolete. (Ingersoll Engineers, 1984, p. 33).

Such findings would be less significant if FMS were replacing special-purpose transfer lines, but other research suggests that this is not the case. A German study found that 85 per cent of FMS had replaced stand-alone NCMT, and only 11 per cent had replaced transfer lines: 'definite, clear-cut developmental trends as far as system flexibility is concerned do not stand out at present . . . the innovation objectives of increasing productivity and reducing through-put times were of greater significance than increasing flexibility. (Fix-Stertz *et al.,* 1987, pp. 70–1).

However, major international variations appear to exist. A comparative

Table 4.7 Comparison of FMS flexibility in the US and Japan

	US	Japan
Number of different parts produced	10	93
Annual volume per part	1,727	258
Number of parts produced per day	88	120
Number of new parts introduced per year	1	22

Source: Jaikumar, 1986

Table 4.8 Number of product variants processed by FMS in Europe, the US and Japan

Number of variants	% of installations		
	Europe	US	Japan
1–10	34	41	27
11–50	49	22	24
51–100	8	13	20
101+	9	24	29
Total	100	100	100

Source: ECE, 1986.

study of FMS in the United States and Japan found that systems in Japan produce almost ten times as many variants as those in the United States, 93 compared with 10. In addition, for every new part produced by an FMS in the United States, 22 were introduced in Japan (Table 4.7). Other surveys of FMS performance reveal similar variations in flexibility: only 17 per cent of FMS in Europe process more than 50 different parts, compared to 37 per cent of systems in the United States, and 49 per cent in Japan (Table 4.8).

Conventional wisdom suggests that the flexibility of FMS is a function of the sophistication of the technology (Browne *et al.*, 1984). But as with stand-alone NCMT, the Japanese appear to favour less sophisticated technology than their counterparts in the West. FMS in the United States and Europe are typically designed for high-precision, small-batch production characterisitic of the defence and aerospace industries, whereas systems in Japan tend to be more simple and suitable for a wider range of applications (Bessant & Haywood, 1985; Hartley, 1984). The number of machining centres per FMS provides a crude indication of system complexity, and this measure indicates that FMS in Japan are less complex than those in the United States and Europe (Table 4.9). The time taken to implement FMS in Japan appears to confirm this: in the United States a

Table 4.9 Number of machines per FMS in Europe, the US and Japan, 1981

No. of machines per FMS	No. of FMS by area		
	Europe	US	Japan
2–5	12	2	18
6–10	13	10	8
11–15	3	4	4
16–25	1	0	2
26+	2	1	0
Average	8	11	7

Source: Bessant & Haywood, 1985.

FMS takes an average of some 25,000 man-hours to conceive, develop, install, and get running; in Japan just 6,000 man-hours are needed (Jaikumar, 1986). The contrast between Japan and Europe is not as great, but Europe includes many different national approaches to FMS. For example, computer control typically accounts for 20 per cent of total FMS cost in the United Kingdom, but only 6 per cent in Sweden (Haywood & Bessant, 1987). Therefore the obsession with technological sophistication may simply be an Anglo-Saxon trait.

The emergence of distinct national rather than global patterns of development and adoption confirms the importance of the context of use and the role of users. Certain options may only exist in specific organisational or national contexts. Case studies suggest that in many cases firms are investing in FMS in an attempt to overcome what are essentially organisational shortcomings. As a result some users have adopted inappropriate technology and have failed to improve their flexibility (Bessant & Haywood, 1985). The evaluation, installation and management of FMS clearly warrants further research (Voss, 1988), as many options may be closed early on:

The limited flexibility of a flexible machining system can, of course, be a disadvantage unless the system and the parts that it is to make have been carefully chosen. Either the system must be designed for a limited product range for which future demand is predictable or it must have, or be capable of having added, more flexibility at the expense of simplicity and cost. In general, a company installing a flexible machining system must be prepared to reorganise its manufacturing procedures if the full potential of the system is to be realised . . . the disadvantages of flexible machining systems are, in many regards, simply a restatement of their advantages. The drawback is not the high capital cost (which may not be higher than that of stand-alone tools), it is the flexibility itself . . . Planning and understanding are crucial because in one way the system is inflexible, as most of the options should be planned at the beginning. (NEDC, 1984, p. 20).

4.3 Industrial robots

No internationally accepted definition of an industrial robot exists, but in practice almost all definitions are similar to that of the British Robot Association: 'An industrial robot is a reprogrammable device designed to both manipulate and transport parts, tools, or specialised manufacturing implements through variable programmed motions for the performance of specific manufacturing tasks' (BRA, 1989). The Japan Industrial Robot Association (JIRA) has traditionally adopted a far broader definition than its counterparts in the West, perhaps because the Japanese are less obsessed with technological novelty. Typically statistics from Japan include manual, fixed-, and variable-sequence manipulators not counted elsewhere, making international comparisons difficult: 'figures include non-programmable manipulators and pick-and-place units and anything else mechanical that moves!' (Rooks, 1987, p. 151). However, since 1984 the JIRA has published two sets of statistics, one based on their own definition, the other excluding manual and fixed-sequence machines (but curiously still including variable-sequence devices). Unless stated otherwise, the statistics used throughout this section have been adjusted to conform as far as possible to international definitions.

The concept of an automatic manipulator for parts-handling originates from the late 1950s and early 1960s like FMS. Again the basic ideas were developed in Britain but were first exploited commercially in the United States. In 1957, a British engineer called Kenwood registered the original patent, whereas the first US patent relating to robotics was Devol's 'Programmed Article Transfer System' registered in 1961 (Baranson, 1983; Mortimer & Rooks, 1987). The Devol patents were purchased by the Consolidated Diesel Engine Company (Condec), which later had to make a cash settlement to Kenwood, acknowledging the importance of his earlier patent. Condec subsequently set up a subsidiary called Unimation (*Uni*versal Auto*mation*) to exploit the patents commercially. Nevertheless Unimation and other early robot manufacturers did not achieve any profits until the late 1970s (Engelberger, 1980). 'Technology push' clearly dominated the initial development of robotics, as no market existed.

Unimation's first commercial customers were the two United States automotive giants, Ford and General Motors, in 1961. These early machines were powered hydraulically and had hard-wired controls, and were therefore only suitable for highly repetitive tasks where the main requirement was brute strength. Consequently they were first applied to the job of die casting, and later to other machine-servicing duties (Engelberger, 1980). The first tool-handling or process robot was developed in 1966 by the Norwegian agricultural equipment company, Trallfa, in response to problems it had experienced in recruiting workers for the unpleasant task of spray painting (Mortimer & Rooks, 1987). In 1969 Unimation installed the first multi-robot spot-welding line at General Motors, but it was not until 1972 that Europe received its first multi-robot line, at Fiat in Italy. In Japan Unimation licensed Kawasaki Heavy Industries to manufacture their robots there in 1967, and the company installed the first spot-welding line at Nissan in 1972 (Cusumano, 1985; Sadamoto, 1981). Investments in multi-robot spot-welding lines in the automobile industry worldwide continued to swell robot numbers during the 1970s, but interestingly Toyota delayed investment in robotics until more 'flexible' devices became available (Cusumano, 1985).

The next significant technological development was the launch of the first commercial, all electric-drive robot by the Swedish firm ASEA in 1973. A year later the first mini-computer-controlled robot was sold by the American machine-tool company Cincinnati-Milacron, and a microprocessor-controlled robot was developed by Victor Scheinman at MIT/VICARM in 1976 (Miller, 1985; Seering, 1987). Unimation reinforced this trend and produced its first electric-drive, microprocessor-controlled robot in 1978. This robot, the PUMA (Programmable Universal Machine for Assembly) was designed specifically for assembly work and was based on the MIT/VICARM research, but the design criteria were specified by their main customer, General Motors.

Unlike earlier Unimates the PUMA was a sophisticated, jointed-arm configuration robot with six controllable motions (degrees of freedom), designed to emulate as far as possible the human arm (Seering, 1987). The West German firm KUKA also introduced the first electric drive robot designed for spot welding in 1978, challenging the slower, less accurate, less reliable, hydraulic welding robots from the United States. In Japan arguably the greatest innovation in industrial robots was the development of the SCARA (Selective Compliance Assembly Robot Arm). In 1978 Professor Makino of Yamanashi University proposed a project to design a low-cost but versatile assembly robot, and this was funded by a consortium of five large Japanese manufacturers, but by the time of the robot's commercial launch in 1981, thirteen Japanese manufactures were involved in the SCARA project. The result was a new, deceptively simple but effective robot configuration, claimed to be suitable for 80 per cent of all industrial assembly work, but costing only half as much as more technologically sophisticated robots like the PUMA (Hartley, 1984; Makino & Furuya, 1985). The parallel with the development of NCMT in Japan is obvious.

During this first decade the industrial robot evolved from a hard-wired controlled hydraulic device suitable only for highly repetitive, relatively simple handling tasks, to a fully programmable electric-drive machine capable of complex assembly work. Nevertheless, apart from more general trends such as the application of microprocessor control, or electric-drive motors, the development of the industrial robot has not followed any single predetermined technological trajectory; rather the evolution of the technology has been intimately related to particular areas of application. Thus the original concept of 'universal automation' had been abandoned, and robots had become increasingly task-specific.

Changes in the robot industry reflect this trend: the steady growth of robot manufacturers during the 1970s was followed by a proliferation of suppliers in the 1980s, as many larger users of industrial robots also became suppliers. Furthermore many users in the United States began to 'add value' to robots manufactured in Japan by developing their own software and systems. In the United States during the early 1980s, Westinghouse acquired Unimation and Condec, General Motors formed the joint-venture GMF Robotics with the Japanese robot manufacturer Fanuc, General Electric subsequently also formed a joint-venture with Fanuc, and IBM designed and marketed its own range of robots, which were manufactured in Japan by Sankyo Seiki. Thus in 1980 the US robot market was dominated by just six suppliers: Unimation, Cincinnati-Milacron, DeVilbiss (Trallfa), ASEA, Prab, and Copperweld accounted for 95 per cent of all domestic sales, but by 1983 the share of these six firms had fallen to just 65 per cent (Conigliaro, 1983). But the US supply market continues to be extremely concentrated, only the actors have changed: in 1980 Unimation was market leader with 44 per cent of sales; in 1984 GMF Robotics had taken the lead with a 31 per cent share of the home market (Mortimer & Rooks, 1987); today just three robot manufacturers dominate the market, GMF Robotics, ABB Robotics (ASEA), and Cincinnati Milacron.

In contrast the robot industry in Japan has remained relatively fragmented, with many users becoming suppliers of the technology based on their in-house experience. In 1980 the market leader in Japan, Kawasaki Heavy Industries, accounted for just 8 per cent of the domestic market (Baranson, 1983); by 1986 Fanuc had taken the lead in Japan but still accounted for less than 14 per cent of domestic robot sales (Robot News, 1986). Today the eight major robot producers account for just a third of the Japanese market. The trend in Europe lies somewhere between the American and Japanese examples, reflecting the heterogeneity of the various countries. Machine-tool builders such as KUKA and major industrial users such as ASEA/ABB Robotics have become robot manufacturers, and more recently European automobile manufacturers have begun to offer commercial robot systems: Acma Robotique (Renault) and Citroën Industrie in France; Comau (Fiat) in Italy; and VW in Germany (Mortimer & Rooks, 1987; OECD, 1983). As robots have become increasingly task-specific a broad supplier base appears to have become more important than a few specialist robot manufacturers. Consequently the initial lead of specialist American robot manufacturers has given way to Japanese user/supplier firms: by 1986 six of the ten largest robot manufacturers worldwide were Japanese, and together accounted for a third of all robot sales (Dataquest, 1988). In addition many Japanese robot manufacturers are involved in collaborative projects with companies in the US and Europe (Yonemoto, 1987).

As industrial robots have become increasingly tied to the needs of particular users, it is possible to identify three distinct stages of development associated with specific generic robot applications: firstly handling tasks

Table 4.10 Population of industrial robots worldwide, 1981–1988

	1981	1982	1983	1984	1985	1986	1987	1988
				(thousands of units)				
FRG	2.3	3.5	4.8	6.6	8.8	12.4	14.9	17.7
Italy	0.5	1.0	1.5	2.6	4.0	5.0	6.6	8.3
France	0.8	1.4	1.9	2.8	4.1	5.3	6.6	8.0
UK	0.7	1.2	1.8	2.6	3.2	3.7	4.3	5.0
Sweden	1.1	1.3	1.5	1.7	2.0	2.4	2.8	3.0
Europe	5.4	8.4	11.5	16.5	22.1	28.8	35.2	42.1
US	6.0	7.0	8.0	13.0	20.0	25.0	29.0	32.6
Japan*	9.7	18.4	32.4	54.9	83.1	106.6	127.9	176.1
Total	21.1	33.8	51.9	84.2	125.2	160.4	192.1	250.8

*Japanese data adjusted to exclude manual & fixed-sequence manipulators.
Source: IFR, 1989; JIRA, 1987.

(where the part is manipulated by the robot, e.g., machine loading) during the 1960s; process tasks during the 1970s (where the tool is manipulated by the robot, e.g., welding or paint spraying); and most recently assembly tasks in the 1980s. This taxonomy is more appropriate and less confusing than the more usual approach of describing robot development in terms of successive 'generations' based on control technology. For example, the OECD and JIRA classify manual and sequential manipulators as 'first-generation' robots. Others describe current playback and numerically controlled devices as 'first-generation' robots, sensor-based robots as 'second-generation', and future 'intelligent' robots as 'third-generation' (Scott, 1984). Similarly in their influencial study Ayres and Miller (1981, 1983) distinguish between existing 'Level I' robots, and future sensor-based 'Level II' robots, and conclude that the former are capable of performing up to 60 per cent of all industrial tasks, and the latter up to 90 per cent. But such studies fail to take into account the increasing specialisation of robots.

The diffusion of industrial robots was slow but steady during the 1970s, but rapid growth followed in the early 1980s as the capabilities of robots improved. There were estimated to be less than 20,000 robots worldwide in 1980, but by 1988 there were more than 250,000 in use (Table 4.10). The falling cost of robots relative to labour has clearly contributed to this impressive growth (Lewis *et al.*, 1984), but the main factor has been the increasing range of robots available for different applications. The OECD study argues that growth:

is mainly determined by the relationship between the costs of robots, the use they are put to, and the expected payback period . . . the increasing sophistication of the technology increases the flexibility (*sic*) of the machinery and therefore alters the investment evaluation. (OECD, 1983, p. 30).

Table 4.11 Density of robots worldwide, 1984–1987

Country	Robot Density (robots per 10,000 employees)	
	1984	1987
Japan	122.6	253.8
Sweden	70.1	86.5
Italy	27.1	37.8
FRG	16.2	40.5
US	14.8	34.6
France	14.7	34.4
UK	8.5	19.7

Source: Edquist & Jacobsson, 1988; IFR, 1988; ECE, 1988.

Table 4.12 Robot density by country and industry, 1987

	Auto	Elec	Mech	Metal
UK	24	11	4	11
Italy	90	11	19	n.a.
France	37	15	23	10
Sweden	531	n.a.	47	71
Japan	236	265	65	39

Source: Employment statistics, ECE, 1988; Robot statistics, as Table 4.13.

This suggests that the price/performance trade-off is paramount, and assumes that flexibility is a function of technological sophistication. But this may not be the case.

In simple numerical terms Japan leads the world in the application of industrial robots. But international 'league tables' must be put into context, and in the case of robots this is normally done by calculating the 'robot density', i.e. the number of robots per 10,000 manufacturing employees. On this basis Italy, France, Germany, and the United States are found to be similar, with Sweden ahead of this group. The greatest contrast is between the United Kingdom and Japan, which are consistently at the two extremes, having the lowest and highest robot densities respectively (Table 4.11). Significant international disparities exist: the robot density in Japan is more than ten times that in the United Kingdom. Many factors may account for this:

various inter-related factors lie behind these different patterns of diffusion: the role of promotional agencies; the opportunities provided by industrial structure, especially the car industry; national labour situations; the vitality of the robotics supply and service infrastructures; and finally the effects of government policies, particularly those aimed specifically at robotics. (Fleck & White, 1984).

The role of industrial structure is perhaps most significant as robots

Table 4.13 Distribution of robots by country and task, 1987

	FRG	Ita.	Fra.	UK	Swe.	US	Japan
	(% of total installations in each country)						
Handling	29	31	33	40	39	45	52
Process	53	40	40	36	33	40	15
Assembly	16	15	12	10	6	14	26
Other*	2	14	15	14	22	1	7
Total	100	100	100	100	100	100	100

*robots for inspection, training, development, and other tasks.
Source: AFRI, 1988; BRA, 1988; FABRIZI, 1988, IPA, 1988; JIRA 1988; RIA, 1988; SWIRA, 1988.

Table 4.14 Density of robots in the UK by size of plant, 1985

Plant size (no. of employees)	Robots	Employees (10,000s)	Density
1–99	385	136.1	2.8
100–199	353	53.9	6.5
200–499	898	87.8	10.0
500–999	545	65.8	8.3
1000+	1027	153.6	6.7
Total	3208	497.6	6.4

Source: BRA, 1986; CSO, 1988; Northcott, 1986.

have become more task-specific, moving away from the original concept of the general purpose 'steel collar' worker or 'universal automation'. In all countries the automobile industry has played a key role in the early development of robots, and in most cases continues to be the largest user of the technology. This is evident when the robot density in various industries is compared (Table 4.12). With the notable exception of Japan, the density of robots is greatest in the automobile industry, reflecting its heavy use of process robots, particularly multi-robot installations for spot-welding and painting. Automobile manufacturers are still major users of robots in Japan, but the electrical industry is now the main user, reflecting the growing importance of assembly robots (Table 4.13).

There has been a trend away from process applications associated with the automobile industry and towards assembly applications in the electrical industry. This has been most pronounced in Japan, but is apparent in most mature economies: in Japan the automobile industry accounted for 38 per cent of all robots in 1979, and the electronics industry for 18 per cent; by 1986 the shares were 17 per cent and 23 per cent respectively (Sadamoto, 1981; Yonemoto, 1987). In the United Kingdom the automotive industry

Table 4.15 Relative flexibility of robots and NCMT

	% installations	
	NCMTs	Robots
Annual production volume		
1–100	15	0
100–1,000	17	0
1,000–10,000	21	7
10,000–100,000	43	58
1,000,000–1m	4	28
1m–10m	0	7
Total	100	100
Number of product variants		
1–5	15	58
6–10	21	16
11–50	26	21
51+	38	5
Total	100	100
Batch size		
1–10	23	0
11–100	30	5
101–1,000	40	28
1,000–10,000	7	42
10,000+	0	25
Total	100	100

Source: ECE, 1985.

used 34 per cent of all robots in 1980, and the electrical sector just 5 per cent; in 1987 the relative shares were 30 per cent and 12 per cent (BRA, 1981, 1989). The massive automobile and consumer electronics industries in Japan have clearly contributed to the widespread adoption of industrial robots in that country, as both users and suppliers of the technology.

It is less clear what affect company size has on the diffusion of industrial robots. The distribution of users in the United Kingdom indicates that the technology has had the greatest impact in 'medium'-sized plants, i.e. those with 200–500 employees (Table 4.14). Research indicates that smaller plants have little to gain through the adoption of robots: 'the application of programmble robots tends to reduce the share of sales accounted for by small firms' (Acs *et al.*, 1988, p. 16). This may be due to the limited flexibility of industrial robots. Some case studies found that: 'the robot, once installed, appears to be just an extension of the dedicated automation' (Hunt & Hunt, 1983, p. 12). Similarly a recent review of robot applications noted that:

compared to NCMT, robots have been used on work where flexibility is less important, e.g., on parts and products produced in larger batch sizes and in larger volumes with less variation and less reprogramming needs. This, however, is almost certainly a consequence of the still limited technical development of robots. (Edquist & Jacobsson, 1988, p. 52).

It is true that industrial robots are generally used in circumstances demanding less flexibility than NCMT, but it is unclear whether this is due to the limitations of existing technology or to users perception of the role of robots in manufacturing (Table 4.15). A survey in the United Kingdom revealed that only a quarter of potential users expected any improvement in manufacturing flexibility, it being ranked less important than improvements to the consistency of production, lower labour costs, and increased output; only 16 per cent of users subsequently claimed any improvement in flexibility (Northcott, 1986, p. 178). However, there may be sound technical reasons for this:

It has often been stated that the greatest virtue of robots lies in their flexibility. The implication is that a manufacturer might best utilize a robot by assuming it to perform a variety of tasks. In fact this almost never occurs. The cost of preparing a robot to perform a single task is very high and is usually not justified unless the robot is to be dedicated to that task. The primary advantage of flexibility brought about by programmability of a robot is that it can be reprogrammed to accommodate small changes in the task to which it has been assigned. (Seering, 1987, pp. 28-9).

In short, technological developments during the 1980s have increased the dexterity of industrial robots and have allowed a wider range of applications to be automated, from simple machine loading to complex assembly tasks. But such developments appear to have had relatively little impact on flexibility. In the 1980s many suppliers and potential users of robots believed that the development of sensor-based, 'second-generation' devices were the key to the widespread adoption of the technology. Today similar claims are being made for so-called 'third generation' systems, based on developments in artificial intelligence (AI). Many companies in the West are banking on such technology to allow them to 'leapfrog' their Japanese competitors:

A decade ago, the Factory of the Future seemed just around the corner . . . It didn't happen that way. Many companies tossed millions of dollars' worth of fancy equipment into their factories and wound up with little to show for it. A hard lesson was learned: All those high-tech gadgets were just too dumb to cut it in an environment plagued by constant change . . . The goal isn't just to work faster, but smarter – with the help of lots of artificial intelligence buried in a new generation of manufacturing systems . . . The Japanese may outclass the US in manufacturing skills, but these few ultra-advanced plants are so far an all-American thrust. (*Business Week*, 8 May 1989)

5

Emerging trajectories: the automation of assembly

To date users of programmable automation have only achieved 'islands of automation' based on NCMT, FMS, and robots. The impact of NCMT and FMS has been confined to machining metal and thus mainly parts fabrication, whilst early robots were only suitable for handling and process applications. Assembly has traditionally represented an automation 'bottle-neck', and in most plants is still labour-intensive. The application of robots promises to remove this final barrier to computer-integrated manufacturing (CIM), but how will this effect manufacturing flexibility? This chapter examines the economics of various options, and reviews early trends in the application of assembly automation.

5.1 Significance of assembly

Most manufacturing processes involve both parts fabrication and the subsequent joining and assembly of these into sub-assemblies and final products. Up till now a great deal of progress has been made in the automation of parts fabrication, but relatively little in assembly. In a typical automobile plant between 50–95 per cent of all metal cutting, forming, welding, and painting processes are automated, but less than 10 per cent of final assembly operations (Weiner, 1985; Krafcik, 1989). Similarly, in the electronics sector automatic parts insertion machines are limited to mount-ing small, regular axial and radial components, but odd-form components are normally still inserted by hand (Tanaka et al., 1985). The OECD estimated that just 5 per cent of all assembly work was fully automated in 1983. As a result assembly typically accounts for over two-thirds of manufacturing costs (Nevins & Whitney, 1980; OECD, 1983). In the automobile and electrical sectors around 70 per cent of all direct labour is in assembly (Table 5.1). But automation can rarely be justified on the basis of labour saving alone, as direct labour may account for just 5–10 per cent of

Table 5.1 Proportion of direct labour involved in assembly

	Italy (1979)	US (1970)
Automobilies	70	67
Electrical	72	74
Light electro-mech.	78	n.a.
Machinery	n.a.	18

Source: ECE, 1985; Nevins & Whitney, 1978.

Table 5.2 Proportion of manufacturing time accounted for by assembly operations in the automobile industry

	1980	1986
Trim & final assembly	27	34
Press shop	13	10
Body shop	25	20
Painting & surface treatment	9	12
Engine & transmission	9	10
Machining & foundry	11	9
Plastics & textiles	6	4
Total	100	100

Source: Schupp, 1988.

total costs. Therefore automation aimed at reducing labour costs may be counter-productive if it results in increased indirect labour and higher overheads (Foyer & Drazan, 1986).

However, in many sectors assembly has become an automation 'bottle-neck' as processes upstream have been automated, and it has been estimated that up to 60 per cent of inventory costs are in assembly areas (Ingersoll Engineers, 1984). In the automotive industry assembly-line methods are used extensively, but assembly still represents the most time-consuming activity: it accounted for around a quarter of all manufacturing time in 1980, but more than a third by 1986 (Table 5.2). This is mainly because most other processes have been automated, but in many cases products have also become more complex. However, labour-intensive assembly is inherently flexible, and to some extent has offset the increasing rigidity of processes upstream: 'the assembly plant is a productive unit that has remained relatively flexible, and consequently the labor content per vehicle has remained constant and has not developed like that in the engine plant' (Abernathy, 1978, p. 159). Therefore the increasing automation of assembly may have a significant impact on manufacturing flexibility.

5.2 Trends in assembly automation

Special-purpose automation

The earliest innovations in assembly were essentially organisational. The assembly line is synonymous with Ford and mass production, but the moving assembly line was introduced some six years after the first Model T was built. At first only the magneto-flywheel was assembled on a simple line, but no conveyors were used. Engineers at Ford divided the assembly of the magneto-flywheel into twenty-nine simple operations and through the division of labour drastically reduced assembly time. Following this early success, the engine, radiator, and many electrical sub-assemblies also began to be assembled on lines. The next developments were in final assembly. Initially the chassis was simply pulled by rope between assembly stations, reducing assembly time by over a half. Finally in 1914, the powered endless conveyor was introduced for chassis assembly, reducing the total assembly time by three-quarters (Abernathy *et al.*, 1981; Boothroyd & Redford, 1968). By that time annual production of the Tin Lizzie had reached 300,000, and peaked at 1.9 million nine years later (Altshuler *et al.*, 1985). The success of the assembly line was based on high-volume, standardised production. It is estimated that more than half of all products are now assembled on lines, although less than 5 per cent are fully automated (OECD, 1983).

The spread of assembly-line methods has facilitated automation. Custom-built, cam-driven and pneumatic-powered assembly machines were the first to be developed, and are still the most commonly used in high-volume production. Line and rotary configurations exist, but the principle is the same in each case: successive assembly machines, or 'stations', insert a part into the assembly. The number of assembly stations needed is simply a function of the number of component parts, rather than production volume. Stations can only perform simple operations, essentially a 'stroke', so an assembly must be broken down into many operations. Such systems are normally *indexed* or *synchronous*, i.e. all the assembly stations are interlocked with each other. The main drawback of such an arrangement is that a problem at any station will affect the whole line. Therefore quality of components and reliability of machines is critical: the reliability of the system is the product of the reliability of each assembly station. For example, if each assembly station has an efficiency (uptime) of 98 per cent, a twenty station indexed system would only be 67 per cent efficient (i.e. 98^{20}). Therefore in practice the number of stations, and hence the total number of parts which can be assembled by such a system is limited (Pham, 1985; Redford & Lo, 1986).

So-called 'memory-pin' machines were an early attempt to overcome some of these limitations. If an insertion was unsuccessful at any station, no further operations would be made on that assembly. Therefore it was no longer necessary to stop an entire line because of a single fault. This increased machine utilisation, but did nothing to reduce the proportion of defective assemblies produced. To achieve this successive stations had to be decoupled to allow time to correct faults as they occurred. In *free-transfer* or *non-synchronous* systems shuttles or pallets are used in place of a fixed transfer line (e.g. conveyor), thus allowing some buffering between work stations. System efficiency is a function of buffer stock size and increases with the size of buffers. In practice a combination of indexed and free-transfer systems are often used, depending on factors such as the number of stations, quality of parts, and complexity of assembly.

Modular-based systems were introduced in the 1960s and represent the first attempt to improve the flexibility of assembly automation. Standard modules allow a greater proportion of an assembly system to be built 'off the shelf', reducing both the cost and time taken to develop a system. In addition the reusability of equipment is improved. It is estimated that modular assembly systems take up to 40 per cent less time to develop than conventional automation, and around a third of the system can be reused following product changes (Heginbotham, 1984). Consequently suppliers had great hopes for such technology: 'automated rather than manual assembly will come not from robots, but from standard modular assembly systems . . . standard assembly machines designed for specific products, sizes, and volumes' (Riley, 1984, p. 3). But in practice the success of modular systems has been limited: modular assembly machines are written off in both engineering and accounting terms over the life of a product, and are normally not reused (Redford & Lo, 1986); a survey of users in the United States revealed that only 2 per cent of assembly systems in use in 1982 were of a modular design, and the remainder were custom-built (Smith & Wilson, 1982).

The most recent development of special-purpose assembly automation illustrates the difference between programmability and flexibility. Microprocessor technology replaced hard-wired controls in the late 1970s, but assembly automation remained inherently inflexible, and changes are limited to the adjustment of 'stops' on pneumatic actuators (Pham, 1985): 'there is sufficient flexibility here to handle requirements for flexibility, which are essentially the addition, deletion, or substitution of one or more components in a basic assembly sequence' (Riley, 1984, p.35). The main advantage to users of programmable systems is the tracing of faults, although the new control technology combined with modular equipment design have enabled suppliers to reduce the cost and time taken to develop assembly systems (Hollingum, 1980). Thus special-purpose assembly automation is still only appropriate in very special cases:

1. Large annual production volumes, preferably greater than 700,000 per year;

2. Few parts in the assembly, preferably less than ten, typically less than twenty;
3. High-quality parts, better than 2 per cent defectives;
4. Few product styles, ideally just one;
5. A long market life, typically greater than three years;
6. Few design changes throughout the life of the product, preferably less than half the number of parts needing new feeding and/or insertion devices (Redford & Lo, 1986).

In short, conventional assembly automation has had limited impact because of the complexity and flexibility of most assembly work, despite the development of modular and programmable systems: 'automatic assembly is a high volume production tool. It is relatively expensive and will usually involve some degree of investment risk. Its broadest applications will come where production of products is measured in millions of annual units' (Riley, 1983, p. 2).

Flexible assembly automation

Industrial robots are the key to flexible assembly automation. Early robots were hard-wired, hydraulic machines suited to highly repetitive handling tasks; in the 1970s robots were widely used in process applications such as welding and painting; and in the 1980s, began to be used in assembly. Robotic assembly is a relatively recent possibility: 'current industrial robots do not have sophisticated controls or sensors to allow modified behaviour in case of difficulty . . . neither are they accurate enough to perform assembly. Many of these limitations are being overcome or soon will be' (Nevins & Whitney, 1978, p. 78). In handling and process applications brute force is the main requirement, but in assembly accuracy and repeatability are more important. In this respect the most significant technological development was the electric-servo drive robot.

Olivetti's SIGMA (*Sistema Integrato Generico di Manipolazione Automatica*) was the first commercially available robot designed for assembly work. Launched in 1975, this modular, gantry-type device achieves good repeatability and a relatively high payload by virtue of its three linear, mutually orthogonal axis. In 1980 another Italian company, DEA (Digital Electronic Automation), launched a similar machine, the PRAGMA assembly robot. DEA applied its experience of coordinate measuring machines to robotics to produce a high-speed device with good repeatability. But both robots adopted a Cartesian configuration, which is inherently restrictive. The jointed-arm or articulated configuration is much more versatile and emulates the design of the human arm having rotary joints at the 'shoulder', 'elbow', and 'wrist' of the robot. Unimation's PUMA (Programmable Universal Manipulator for Assembly), launched in

1978, was the first and most radical example of this type of robot. The PUMA is a fully programmable, microprocessor-controlled, all-electric drive robot. It is very versatile but because of its configuration and number of electrically powered joints has a limited repeatability and payload. As a result the PUMA has been criticised for being too versatile and sophistciated for most industrial applications (Seering, 1987).

In contrast the SCARA (Selective Compliance Assembly Robot Arm) robot is a much simpler device. Conceived by Professor Makino and developed by a consortium of companies in Japan, the SCARA was launched in 1981. Five potential users and suppliers originally funded the project, but by the time of its launch thirteen companies had been involved in its development. The aim was to produce a robot that was more versatile than Cartesian robots such as the SIGMA and PRAGMA, but cheaper and less sophisticated than other articulated configurations like the PUMA. This was achieved through a simple but ingenious horizontal jointed-arm configuration using just two servo-motors. Thus the SCARA is significantly cheaper than conventional jointed-arms robots, but has a large work envelope and is more versatile than Cartesian designs. The unique configuration has natural mechanical compliance in the horizontal plane to correct for lateral errors, but is very rigid in the vertical direction. As a result the SCARA is claimed to be suitable for around 80 per cent of all assembly work (Makino & Furuya, 1985).

A proliferation of commercial assembly robots followed in the 1980s, most based on the SCARA or PUMA concept (Table 5.3). In 1980 only three different assembly robots were commercially available, but by the end of the decade more than fifty models were on the market (Simons, 1980; Mortimer & Rooks, 1987). As with FMS, many users have also become suppliers of the technology: Bosch, Comau, GEC, GM Fanuc, Hitachi, IBM, Panasonic, Sony, Toshiba, and Yamaha all market their own assembly robots. There has also been a trend towards complete robotic assembly systems, rather than stand-alone robots, such as FAST (Flexible Assembly STation) from ABB Robotics, the 7575 and 7576 'Manufacturing Systems' from IBM, and Sony's SMASH (Sony Multiple Assembly System with High flexibility) system.

The trend towards complete robotic assembly systems reflects the importance of ancillary equipment such as parts feeders and fixtures. Such equipment typically accounts for between a third and half of total system costs, and tends to be product-specific, thus limiting flexibility. Recent attempts to overcome this problem include multi-part feeders, programmable feeders, and sensor-based feeding systems and parts-orientation devices (Redford & Lo, 1986). In theory a very wide range of system options exist, suitable for many different types of application (Table 5.4). But in practice such devices are too expensive for most applications, and most sensor-based systems are still custom-built (Dodd, 1988).

More fundamentally, two basic system options exist: cell or parallel

Table 5.3 Specifications of typical assembly robots

Manufacturer & nationality	Model	Type	Year intro.	Repeatability (mm)	Maximum payload (kg)
Olivetti (Italy)	SIGMA	Gantry	1975	0.10	10
Unimation (US)	PUMA 550	Articulated	1978	0.10	2
DEA (Italy)	PRAGMA	Gantry	1980	0.025	6
Fanuc (Japan)	'A' series	Articulated	1981	0.05	10
Toshiba (Japan)	Tosman	SCARA	1981	0.05	8
Hitachi (Japan)	A3020	SCARA	1983	0.05	2
Adept (US)	Adept 1	SCARA	1985	0.05	6
ABB (Sweden)	IRB1000	Articulated	1985	0.10	3
IBM (US/Japan)	7575	SCARA	1985	0.025	5
	7576	SCARA	1985	0.05	10

Source: Mortimer & Rooks, 1987; *Automation,* January 1990.

assembly, which is analogous to manual bench assembly, with a single robot assembling a complete product, so that the cycle time becomes a function of the number of parts in each complete assembly; and line or series assembly, which is analogous to special-purpose or the classic assembly-line layout, with each robot inserting a single part so the cycle time is constant and equal to the time taken to perform the most complex operation. Flexibility can be incorporated in either configuration, provided that the need is identified at the design stage (Worthington, 1985). In practice, hybrid systems are often designed, in which each robotic station performs two or three assembly operations before transfer to the next station (Redford & Lo, 1986). Generally robots used on an assembly line do not need to be as sophisticated as those in robotic assembly cells:

1. Robots used in line-assembly systems will not generally need the same degree of maneouvrability or 'intelligence' as those used in cells;
2. Each station requires presentation of the parts more frequently than a cell, which reduces costs because parts feeders are generally much faster than assembly robots;
3. With good product design, and appropriate sequencing of tasks, robots should not require any time-consuming gripper changes due to the limited number of operations performed at each station;
4. The special-purpose part of the system is smaller per product assembled than in cell assembly (Redford & Lo, 1986).

It is often assumed that the main barriers to the widespread adoption of robotic assembly have been technological: 'the main obstacle to the

Table 5.4 Options for robotic assembly systems

Robots:	Configuration, number of axis, payload, repeatability, & speed
Parts feeding & orientation devices:	Conventional tracks, vibratory bowls, etc. Multi-part vibratory bowls, etc. Palletised kits of identical parts Palletised kits for a complete product Programmable parts feeders Random parts bins + vision system
Gripper or tool design:	Multi-arm with dedicated tools Multiple tools on turret wrist Universal socket + tool changes Univeral gripper
Sensors:	Robot or fixture mounted Proximity/optical Force Tactile Vision
Transfer system:	Manual Indexed rotary or line transfer Free-transfer line AGVs

Source: Owen, 1985; Redford & Lo, 1986.

widespread diffusion of assembly robots has hitherto been of a technical nature . . . facilities like tactile sensors, optical (*sic*) sensors, and versatile gripping devices are therefore essential for robot-based assembly' (Edquist & Jacobsson, 1988, p. 50). Sophisticated technologies may be necessary for assembly cells, but half of all products are made on assembly lines (OECD, 1983). Less complex technology may be more appropriate in such circumstances.

5.3 Economics of flexible assembly

The most basic choice is between manual, robotic, and special-purpose assembly methods, but the wide range of robotic systems makes any rigorous evaluation difficult. Simulation software and expert systems to assist system design and evaluation continue to be developed, but to date none can deal with more than a few alternatives. The earliest and still most common approach is based on the 'price time product', that is, the cost of

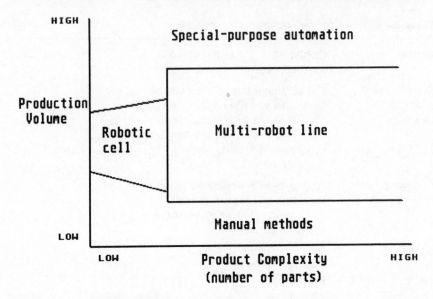

Figure 5.1 Techno-economic model of different types of assembly automation
Source; Boothroyd, 1985

the assembler (manual, dedicated, or programmable) multiplied by the average assembly time per part (Nevins & Whitney, 1980). This indicates that robotic assembly fits neatly between manual methods and conventional assembly automation. For example, it is widely quoted that robotic assembly is most appropriate for annual production volumes of 300,000–3,000,000, the precise domain depending on the relative cost of labour and robots (Lynch, 1977; Nevins & Whitney, 1978). Similarly a recent text on the subject states that 'the most important conclusion to be drawn here is that the various systems do not compete with each other; by far the most important parameter in selecting the correct system is the annual production volume' (Redford & Lo, 1986, p. 14).

More sophisticated approaches attempt to evaluate the effect of other variables. Boothroyd (1985) models the relationship between production volume, product complexity, and method of assembly. For example, for an assembly of twenty parts, and a payback of six shift-years (i.e., two shifts over three years, or three shifts over two years), a robotic assembly cell would be most appropriate for annual volumes of 45,000–65,000 per shift, a two-robot cell for 65,000–160,000 per shift, and a multi-station robotic assembly line for higher volumes. This suggests that robotic systems may compete with manual methods at lower volumes than indicated by earlier models (Figure 5.1).

However, Boothroyd's model does not take flexibility into account and is only valid where a single product or family of products is assembled. Where many product variants are assembled in relatively small batches (e.g., a

Table 5.5 Annual production of assembled products

Annual production*	% of all products
3m.+	5
1m.–3m.	9
500,000–1m.	12
150,000–500,000	16
100,000–150,000	25
25,000–100,000	16
< 25,000	17
	100

*Derived from cycle time assuming two-shift production.
Source: Holmqvist, 1985.

different product every shift), robotic assembly cells could become economic at much lower production volumes, perhaps as low as 10,000 units a year (Redford & Lo, 1986). Conversely, robotic assembly lines could compete with special-purpose automation in high-volume, high-variety production. It has been calculated that robotics could be competitive with conventional automation at annual production volumes of up to five million, assembling just ten different product variants (Csakvary, 1981).

Therefore robots may be appropriate for a much wider range of assembly application than commonly believed. The main factors affecting the economics of robotic assembly are: *scale* — robotic assembly may be appropriate at lower production volumes than conventional assembly automation; *complexity* — the dexterity of robots allows more complex assembly work to be automated; and *flexibility* — robotics can assemble products having many variants, as well as those having short life cycles. But in practice no robotic assembly system will possess all of these abilities, so trade-offs will reflect production priorities.

Of these factors, flexibility is the key to the widespread adoption of the technology. Annual production volumes do not appear to represent a significant problem (Table 5.5) and suggest that up to two-thirds of all products could be assembled by robot. In the automobile industry almost half of all assemblies are produced in annual volumes of between 100,000 and 200,000, and therefore might be suitable for robotic assembly (IPA, 1984). The effect of product complexity is less clear. Many factors influence the complexity of assembly: the number, weight, size, shape, tolerance, and rigidity of parts, as well as location and methods of joining. For example, the payload of a typical assembly robot is less than 10kg, which would limit applications in certain sectors more than others (Table 5.6). Taking other factors into account indicates that existing assembly robots could only perform around 10 per cent of final assembly operations in the automotive industry (Arai, 1988). However, the complexity of

Table 5.6 Average weight of parts handled by robot

Sector	Weight (lb.)
Electrical/electronic	3
Aerospace	10
Light manufacturing	10
Automotive	25
Casting	40
Heavy manufacturing	60
All industries	20

Source: Smith & Wilson, 1982.

Table 5.7 Sectoral distribution of assembly automation in the US (1982) and proportion of programmable stock

	All	Programmable*	% Prog.
Electrical	4,770	1,067	22
Metal products	4,632	862	19
Automobile	2,782	160	6
Machinery	2,040	705	35
Other	3,884	134	3
Total	18,108	2,928	16

*Figures for programmable assembly machines include small number of assembly robots (less than 100).
Source: American Machinist, 1983.

assembly can in many cases be reduced by appropriate product design (Boothroyd & Dewhurst, 1983), so the potential for robotic assembly may be far greater than this. It is difficult to assess the significance of flexibility, but the diffusion of conventional assembly automation indicates that this may have been a major limiting factor (Table 5.7).

5.4 Early patterns of adoption

The increasing availability of commercial assembly robots during the 1980s resulted in many predictions of the widespread automation of assembly (Table 5.8). In fact assembly was the fastest growing robot application in the 1980s, albeit from a small base. In the United Kingdom there were estimated to be just thirty-two assembly robots in use in 1982, but by 1988 there were almost 500 (BRA, 1984, 1989). In Japan almost half of all robots installed between 1983 and 1988 were for assembly (Sthen, 1985;

Table 5.8 Forecasts of the impact of robotic assembly

Study	% products assembled by robot or % assembly workers displaced
Ingersoll Engineers (1980)	1%
Ayres & Miller/Carnegie-Mellon (1981)	3–50%
Hunt & Hunt (1983)	1–3%
Smith & Wilson/Delphi (1982)	50%
OECD (1983)	2–40%

Table 5.9 Proportion of robots used for assembly

	1980	1983	1987
FRG	4	5	16
Italy	n.a.	12	15
France	n.a.	7	12
UK	1	6	10
US	1	4	14
Japan	7*	15	26

*Estimate for 1981.
Source: AFRI, 1988; BRA, 1988; Fabrizi, 1988; IPA, 1988; JIRA, 1987; RIA, 1988.

IFR, 1989). Today assembly typically accounts for 10–15 per cent of all robots in use worldwide, although handling and welding are still the most common applications in most countries (Table 5.9). But despite such rapid growth the technology has failed to have the impact predicted by early forecasts.

The high cost of assembly robots compared to labour is in many cases still a significant barrier to the widespread adoption of the technology (Miller, 1985b), and in addition some technological limitations still remain (Taylor, 1986). However, a major reason for the limited success of robotic assembly to date appears to be the perception of potential users. Early forecasts were based on the assumption that robots would replace labour-intensive batch assembly, and indeed most subsequent assessments assume that robots will replace labour, rather than conventional assembly automation (Lewis *et al.*, 1984; Bjorkman & Ekdahl, 1988). But manual bench assembly accounts for less than half of all products assembled, and in most cases sophisticated robotics technology would be needed to automate this. In contrast, the most likely candidates for robotic assembly are high-volume, high-variety production, currently dominated by the assembly line and conventional automation:

> while the economics of a robot invariably are first compared with manual operation it is probably more relevant to consider the cost of using hard automation . . . the high cost may deter all but those who can make use of the greater flexibility of the robot compared with hard automation. (Ward, 1980, p. 53)

In this respect users in different countries appear to be adopting divergent philosophies.

In the United States the emphasis has been on relatively sophisticated technology designed to perform complex tasks. General Motors (GM) has long been at the 'leading edge' of advanced automation: the first Unimate robot was used at GM; the PUMA was designed to GM's specification; and in 1982 GM estimated it would be using 10,000 industrial robots by 1988, 3,200 of which would be for assembly (Hunt & Hunt, 1983). As a result GM formed the joint venture GMF Robotics with the Japanese robot manufacturer Fanuc, but later cancelled plans for additional robots. In 1988 GM was using just 5,600 robots (Dodd, 1988), reflecting 'increasing scepticism and growing unease' in the United States with assembly robots (Riley, 1984).

In Europe no dominant trend has yet emerged, but national patterns of adoption are apparent. In the United Kingdom users have attempted to automate batch assembly using relatively sophisticated robotic cells, and the success of this approach will be examined in detail in chapter 6. But probably the most publicised user of robots in Europe is Fiat of Italy. The 'Robogate' welding system at the Rivalta plant, developed by Comau for the Strada car in the late 1970s was made famous in the television advertisements and formed the basis of the 'built by robot' claim. However, the initial efforts to improve the efficiency of assembly operations at Fiat were not based on robots, but centred on the LAM (*Lavorazione Asincrone Motore*) or 'asynchronous engine assembly' system. This was introduced during the early 1980s, consisted of numerous manual assembly stations connected by AGVs, and was coordinated by computer. This system was very flexible and accommodated a wide range of different assemblies, but failed to deliver any significant improvement in productivity.

Fiat has since concentrated on reducing product complexity and the number of variations to facilitate automation of assembly. Since 1980 Fiat has reduced the number of chassis manufactured from nine to five, and the number of different body styles from nine to six (Fiat Auto S.p.A., 1987). At the FIRE (Fully Integrated Robotised Engine) plant in Termoli, Fiat has claimed to have automated 90 per cent of production using fifty-six robots and ninety-two 'programmable handlers', but flexibility is very limited. Most recently Fiat has automated around a quarter of all operations in final assembly at its plant in Cassino using more than 400 robots and a workforce of 7,000. But much of the equipment used is custom-built and the plant is dedicated to a single model, the Tipo, which currently has few variants.

Volkswagen has adopted a similar approach to Fiat. Hall 54 at Wolfsburg, once claimed to be the most automated assembly plant in the World, is probably VW's most famous plant, with some 30 per cent of final assembly operations automated. This high level of automation was achieved using mostly special-purpose equipment, and the plant is dedicated to the Golf and its variants. In contrast VW's new showcase plant at Emden is claimed to be highly flexible, and employs a work-force of 10,000 together with more than 500 robots to assemble all variants of the Golf and Passat models. But such high levels of assembly automation are uncommon, and on average automobile plants in Europe use less automation than their counterparts in Japan and the United States. More importantly the philosophy behind such automation appears to be very different:

while Western plants lag in the introduction of simple automation applications, they are on par with or ahead of their Japanese counterparts in automating complex processes requiring substantial investments in highly specialised equipment . . . we have found Japanese automation to be consistently more flexible than that in plants of US or European parentage. (Krafcik, 1989, pp. 10–1)

In Japan relatively simple SCARA-type assembly robots are the most commonplace, and are used extensively by all manufacturers of consumer electronics: Sony, Pioneer, Toshiba, Matsushita (National Panasonic, Technics), Hitachi, and Mitsubishi Electric (Makino & Yamafuji, 1985). But in areas demanding the use of more sophistcated robotics application is limited. Nissan currently uses robots at its showcase Zama plant to install batteries, window glass, seats, rear doors, lamps, and spare tyres into its current range of cars, but plans to be able to automate around 50 per cent of all final assembly operations as soon as new models which have been designed for robotic assembly are introduced (Bairstow, 1986, p. 28). Honda aims to go further still, and plan to integrate its existing 150 assembly processes into just fifty, using hybrid electric-hydraulic robots to automate 80 per cent of these operations (*Japan Economic Journal*, 27 December 1986). In contrast to the trend in Europe and the United States where a few, highly automated show plants exist alongside many plants having very little assembly automation, manufacturers in Japan have consistently automated simpler tasks (Krafcik, 1989). The Japanese experience will be discussed in detail in Chapter 7.

National patterns of adoption clearly differ, and many options still exist. But such anecdotal evidence suggests no distinct international 'best practice': 'one of the foremost important perspectives of this subject is an understanding of just how early on in the developing field of robotic development we actually are' (Rathmill, 1985). Subsequent chapters contrast the approach adopted by users in the United Kingdom and Japan, arguably the least and most successful respectively.

6

Technology push: the British experience

In terms of robot density the United Kingdom is at the bottom of the international league table. Assembly was the fastest growing robot application in all industrialised economies during the 1980s, but the proportion of robots used for assembly is much smaller in the United Kingdom than overseas. This chapter identifies the reasons for the relatively poor diffusion of robotic assembly in the United Kingdom, and assesses the impact the technology has had on users' flexibility.

6.1 Growth in robotic assembly

The application of robotics to assembly began in the 1980s. Before that only special-purpose automation was available, and such technology was only appropriate for relatively simple tasks and high-volume, standardised products. Consequently its impact in the United Kingdom has been limited; there were estimated to be only 3,500 special-purpose assembly machines in use in 1982 (Metalworking Production, 1983). Such technology is most commonly used in those sectors characterised by high-volume production, in particular the automobile industry (Table 6.1). But high-volume production is not synonymous with large plants. In fact special-purpose assembly machines are concentrated in plants with less than 200 employees (Table 6.2). Such 'hard automation' is commonly used by sub-contractors in the automotive and electronic components sector as it is most suited to the assembly of small, relatively simple products in large volumes.

Thus the potential for robotic assembly in the early 1980s was considerable. As in other countries, the growth in the United Kingdom has been rapid, albeit from a very small base: in 1980 there were just five robotic assembly installations, but by 1988 almost 500 assembly robots were in use (Table 6.3). In fact in common with trends worldwide, assembly was the fastest growing robot application of the 1980s. But despite this impressive

Table 6.1 Distribution of special-purpose assembly machines by industry in the UK, 1982

Industry	No. of machines	Density*
Motor vehicles & parts	303	10.1
Electronic goods	460	7.3
Other manufacturing	2,650	5.4
All	3,413	5.8

*Density is the number of machines per 10,000 employees.
Source: Metalworking Production, 1983; CSO, 1988.

Table 6.2 Distribution of special purpose assembly machines by plant size in the UK, 1982

No. of employees	No. of plants with special-purpose mach.	Average no. of machines per plant	Density of machines
0–99	240	4	7.1
100–199	58	14	15.1
200–499	130	4	5.9
500–999	71	10	10.8
1,000+	46	7	2.1
Total	545	6	6.9

Source: Metalworking Production, 1983; CSO, 1988.

growth, the impact in absolute terms has been limited. The majority of plants adopting robotic assembly during the 1980s aquired the technology in order to assess its potential, rather than for use in production. In 1987 around a third of users had just one assembly robot and over half of plants only two machines (Tidd, 1988a). There were estimated to be only 130 plants in Britain using robots for assembly in 1985 (Northcott *et al.*, 1986), and probably around 200 plants in 1988. As a result, in 1987 the density of robots in assembly work was half that of all applications, and significantly less than in more mature robot applications such as welding (Table 6.4). Clearly experience of robotic assembly in the United Kingdom is still limited.

Many structural factors have contributed to the low rate of adoption of assembly robots in the United Kingdom: a declining manufacturing sector; relatively low labour costs; weak indigenous robot supply and service sector; and government policies primarily concerned with innovation rather than the diffusion of existing technology (Fleck & White, 1984; Fleck, 1987a). Such factors may help to account for the low density of robots in

Table 6.3 Growth of robotic assembly in the UK, 1980–1988

Year	Total no. of robots	Assembly	% of total
1980	371	5	1.3
1981	713	15	2.1
1982	1,152	32	2.8
1983	1,753	103	5.9
1984	2,623	199	8.2
1985	3,208	294	9.2
1986	3,683	348	9.4
1987	4,303	435	10.1
1988	5,034	493	9.8

Source: BRA, 1982–1989.

Table 6.4 Robot density in assembly, welding and all engineering applications in the UK, 1987

	Operatives	Robots	Density*
Assembly	204,378	435	21
Welding	19,307	1,122	581
All engineering	778,854	3,332	43

*Density is defined as number of robots per: 10,000 operatives.
Source: EITB, 1988; robot statistics, BRA, 1988.

British industry, but they fail to explain why such a relatively small proportion of robots are used for assembly: as shown earlier, the proportion of industrial robots used for assembly in the United Kingdom is smaller than that in any other OECD country.

On the contrary, government support and supply-side factors have encouraged the adoption of robotic assembly in the United Kingdom. In 1980 the government pursuaded Unimation to locate its European manufacturing facility in the United Kingdom, and the company has since produced the PUMA assembly robot there (although the plant has changed ownership). In addition a fifth of all projects funded under the Robotics Support Programme (1982–5) were for robotic assembly. Similarly, supply-side factors do not appear to have been a significant constraint. Although there are few domestic manufacturers of assembly robots, more than a hundred different models can be purchased from UK suppliers (Mortimer & Rooks, 1987). This suggests that deficiencies on the demand-side may be more important.

Table 6.5 Sectoral distribution of plants using robots for assembly in the UK, 1987

Industry	Assembly Robots	Density*
Electrical/electronic	147	2.6
Mechanical	96	1.3
Transport	70	1.3
Plastic products	26	1.3
Metal products	26	0.9
Other	70	0.2
All	435	0.9

*Density is number of assembly robots per 10,000 employees.
Source: Tidd, 1988a; BRA, 1988; CSO, 1988.

6.2 Patterns of adoption

As in other countries the initial diffusion of robots in the United Kingdom is associated with the the automobile industry, and in particular the use of handling and process robots. Today the automotive sector is still the main user of robots, reflecting the large number of welding robots in use, and accounts for about 30 per cent of all installations in the United Kingdom (BRA, 1989). But more recently the electrical/electronics sector has also become a significant user of robotics, due to the availability of assembly robots. This sector only accounts for around 10 per cent of all types of robot in use, but is by far the main user of robotic assembly (Table 6.5).

One reason for this is the limitation of current robotics technology. To achieve the high repeatability required for assembly work, most assembly robots are driven electrically rather than hydraulically. This limits the weight of components which can be manipulated (the maximum 'payload'), and the reach of such machines (the 'work envelope'). Taking into account the additional weight of the gripper or tools, the maximum payload of a typical assembly robot is just a few kilograms. This does not represent a major constraint in electrical or electronics assembly, but represents a major limitation in other industries. It has been estimated that over two-thirds of all components handled by robot are less than five kilograms in the electrical/electronics sector, but less than a fifth of components in the automobile industry (Smith & Wilson, 1982). But the weight of components is only one factor. For example, in the United Kingdom the plastics industry accounts for almost a fifth of all types of robot in use, but only around 5 per cent of all assembly robots (BRA, 1989; Tidd, 1988a).

The contrast between the density of applications in the electronics/electrical industry and other sectors suggests that product complexity may be an important factor. Much electronics assembly is essentially two-dimensional and consists of inserting components in printed circuit boards

Table 6.6 Use of robotic assembly by plant size in the UK, 1987

No. of employees	All robots		Assembly robots	
	No.	Density*	No.	Density*
0–99	430	3.2	26	0.2
100–199	688	12.8	26	0.5
200–499	990	11.3	83	0.9
500–999	645	9.8	70	1.1
1,000+	1,549	10.1	231	1.5
Total	4,303	8.6	435	0.9

*Density is the number of robots per 10,000 employees.
Source: Tidd, 1988a; CSO, 1988.

(pcbs); but mechanical assembly is inherently three-dimensional and more difficult to automate. This may explain the remarkable consistency in the application of robotic assembly outside the electronics sector. Many products can be designed to facilitate automation, and guidelines are widely available and continue to be developed, particularly software-based packages (e.g. Boothroyd & Dewhurst, 1983). Experience indicates that design for assembly can reduce the number of components by up to two-thirds, and also improves product reliability. However, in practice few companies in the United Kingdom adopt such procedures (Miller & Grocock, 1988), and less than half of the products currently assembled by robot were designed for automated assembly (Tidd, 1988a). This clearly limits the widespread adoption of robotic assembly.

Early forecasts of the adoption of robotic assembly assumed that the greatest impact would be in small firms characterised by batch assembly. However, the technology is most commonly used in large plants, and this size-bias is even more significant than for more mature robot applications (Table 6.6). Plants with more than 500 employees account for about half of all robots in use, but more than two-thirds of all assembly robots. This probably reflects the relative immaturity of robotic assembly in the United Kingdom, rather than any scale requirements. To date no dominant mode of production has emerged, and the technology is currently used in both small-batch and high-volume assembly (Table 6.7). Therefore other factors must be responsible for the low level of adoption in the United Kingdom.

6.3 Organisation and implementation

The precise relationship between production technology, organisation, and performance is uncertain. Early studies suggest that technology is the main determinant of organisational structure (Woodward, 1965, 1970), but

Table 6.7 Use of robotic assembly in the UK by production volume and batch size, 1987

Annual production volume	% installations
<100,000	27
100,000–250,000	23
250,000–500,000	15
500,000–1 million	23
1 million+	12
Total	100

Batch size	
<10	12
10–100	8
100–1,000	36
1,000–5,000	24
5,000+	20
Total	100

Source: Tidd, 1988a.

subsequent research found that factors such as size and nationality were of greater significance (Pugh, 1985). More recently, the experience of plants adopting advanced manufacturing technologies indicates that a range of organisational options may exist. Concepts such as 'design space' have been introduced to describe this (Bessant, 1983). In the case of industrial robots it has been argued that:

options exist with respect to the way tasks are organised into jobs . . . robotised cells lend themselves to the introduction of 'autonomous groups' as used in the Volvo Kalmar plant, and to the introduction of Japanese style working practices . . . However, it is equally possible for the necessary system monitoring, operating and ancillary tasks to be organised into isolated and trivial jobs. (Fleck, 1987b, pp. 23–4)

This suggests that existing organisational structures influence the adoption of technology, in contrast to the more usual idea of technology having an 'impact' on organisations. Several case studies have found that users of a wide range of AMT have adopted the technology as a 'technological fix' for organisational problems, including CAD (Arnold, 1983) and NCMT (Buchanan and Boddy, 1983), FMS (Bessant & Haywood, 1985), and industrial robots (Fleck, 1983). But such an approach is unlikely to result in an optimal solution. In most cases designers of robotic assembly systems in the United Kingdom must assume that operators will receive little training, that products will not be designed for automated assembly, and that component quality will be poor.

In the United Kingdom systems are normally engineered to be 'idiot-proof', so that most decisions and variability are removed from the operator. Few users train operators to carry out routine maintenance, clear machine blockages, or to amend programmes, although some larger users have introduced new positions such as 'operator-setter' or 'operator-technician'. Typically an operator will simply load components, carry out some assembly, and remove completed assemblies from a cell. But this makes little sense. For example, it has been estimated that 80 per cent of machine faults take just 20 per cent of total repair time and with appropriate training such minor faults could be corrected by operators. Furthermore as robotic assembly is no faster than manual methods, this approach makes financial justification very difficult (Tidd, 1988b).

The most common methods of justification are simple payback and return on investment criteria based on savings in direct labour. On this basis it is almost impossible to justify robotic assembly for single-shift production, and justification is often marginal for two-shifts. Consequently some two-thirds of current systems are operated for at least two shifts (Tidd, 1988a). In practice some pretty creative accounting is required to justify a robotic assembly cell (Clarke, 1989). Some larger companies have been prepared to ease their normal financial requirements to gain experience of the technology, consistent with their long-term goal of CIM. Some smaller users have received funding under the Robot Support Programme, but this was withdrawn in 1985. Small firms have also adopted robotic assembly in order to win or retain important customers, particularly in the automotive sector: in one case an installation was financed from a company's marketing budget (Tidd, 1988a). But smaller firms face a more fundamental problem, as a recent survey revealed: 'in all cases a lack of trained staff to implement automation was a barrier' (Miller & Grocock, 1988).

Almost without exception users underestimate the time and cost of implementation. Firms of all sizes have experienced problems, and the average system in the United Kingdom has taken four engineering man-years to design, install, and get running. Less than 40 per cent of assembly systems are implemented within a year, compared to 80 per cent of other robot applications. Many so-called 'turn-key' systems subsequently require in-house engineering and development. In certain cases it has taken up to nine months to rewrite and debug software provided; in others tooling and fixtures have had to be re-engineered. Some of these problems are the fault of consultants attempting to apply a standard solution in a wide range of situations, most commonly the 'generic assembly cell'. But more frequently difficulties are the result of the organisational shortcomings of users.

In the United Kingdom design and manufacturing (production) engineers have completely different cultures. Typically design engineers are responsible for product function and performance, and manufacturing engineers for manufacturability, and there is very little formal interaction between the two groups. In addition manufacturers rarely influence the design or quality of bought-in components, and choose suppliers on the

Table 6.8 Robots and sensors used for assembly in the UK, 1987

Type of robot	Example	%
Articulated	Unimation PUMA	64
SCARA	Toshiba SR	16
Cartesian	DEA Pragma	13
Cylindrical	Fanuc A Series	7
Total		100
Type of sensor		
Proximity		35
Vision		31
Tactile		16
Force		9
None		9
Total		100

Source: Tidd, 1988a.

basis of cost and delivery. Consequently many problems which first appear in production can be traced to processes upstream: *assembly* becomes *fitting*, making automation difficult and costly. But as Ford recognised, there can be no fitters in efficient manufacturing.

6.4 Technological trajectories

Relatively sophisticated technology is required to overcome the organisational shortcomings of users in the United Kingdom. Almost three-quarters of installations in the United Kingdom are robotic assembly cells, rather than multi-robot lines. This bias towards robotic assembly cells cannot easily be justified on the basis of cost or scale. As noted in the previous chapter, a cell tends to require more sophisticated robotics technology than a line configuration, and tooling and peripheral equipment, which typically accounts for between a third and a half of total system costs, must also be more sophisticated and costly. Some two-thirds of the assembly robots in use are of the articulated type, the most common example being Unimation's PUMA. Complex multi-gripper arrangements and tool changes are also commom, and almost a quarter use programmable or sensor-based parts feeders (Tidd, 1988a). In addition most installations incorporate some form of sensing, albeit simple proximity devices, and almost a third rely on machine vision (Table 6.8).

A great deal has been made of the advantages of computer integration over 'islands of automation' (e.g. Kaplinsky, 1984), but a robotic assembly cell is a textbook example of such an island. Despite much rhetoric to the contrary, integration is still limited: three-quarters of firms using robotic assembly also use Computer Aided Design (CAD), more than half use Material Requirements Planning (MRP), and over a third automatic testing or inspection. Many users claim CIM to be a long-term objective, but only 16 per cent have DNC links, and less than 10 per cent have integrated robotic assembly with CAD (Tidd, 1988a).

Inappropriate product design, low quality of components, and the desire to minimise operator intervention all increase the level of technology required. As noted earlier, less than half of the products currently assembled by robot were designed for automated assembly, and as a result assembly is often a complex fitting operation requiring what have been described as 'hammer and file' techniques (Burton & Ford, 1985). This limits the widespread application of the technology and helps to explain the preference for relatively sophisticated technology. However, such sophistication does not necessarily improve manufacturing flexibility. For example, machine vision systems usually require special light sources, high optical contrast between parts and background, accurate positioning of cameras, and complex programming. Thus flexibility is often sacrificed for robustness and reliability. In fact there is a significant correlation between the sophistication of the technology and the complexity of assembly task, but none between technological sophistication and flexibility (Tidd, 1989).

6.5 Impact on flexibility

It is desirable to differentiate between the impact of programmable automation and the more general benefits of conventional forms of automation. Arguably the former has the potential to improve overall competitiveness, whereas the latter simply increase productivity. It is also possible to distinguish between *technical* success and broader and more important *business* success, which will depend on the benefits realised by users such as improved product quality, reduced work-in-progress, shorter lead times, and greater flexibility (Voss, 1985, 1988). For example a study of early robot applications in the United Kingdom found that 44 per cent of firms initially experienced technical failure, and 22 per cent abandoned the projects altogether. But several 'sucessful' users subsequently went into receivership or suffered serious financial difficulties (Fleck, 1983).

Almost all robotic assembly systems are successful in the narrow technical sense, despite problems during implementation. However, there is less evidence that the technology has made any significant contribution to business success or competitiveness. Increased productivity and quality are the main benefits claimed by users of robotic assembly (Table 6.9). Assembly robots are generally no faster than manual assembly so the main source of productivity increases is the elimination of unproductive time. This includes lost production during the third shift, weekends, holidays,

Table 6.9 Benefits claimed by users of robotic assembly in the UK

	% Plants with benefit		
	None	Some	Great
Increased productivity	12	44	44
Better quality	16	37	47
Improved process control	50	34	16
Better use of materials/less scrap	41	47	12
Greater flexibility for volume change	56	28	16
Less work in progress/inventory	66	12	22
Greater flexibility for product change	66	22	12
Reduced lead time	66	25	9

Source: Tidd, 1988a.

and due to sick leave; the 'rule of thumb' is that operatives are only productive for half the time (Myrup Andreason & Ahm, 1988). Therefore significant productivity improvements can be achieved provided a system can run unattended over three shifts. But few robotic assembly systems in the United Kingdom can operate without supervision, and less than a third run for three shifts (Tidd, 1988a). Similarly users claim improvements in product quality, but automation can only increase the consistency of assembly. In fact robotic assembly demands higher-quality components and greater attention to product design, and most improvements in product quality can be traced to such factors rather than to the technology *per se.*

Few users in the United Kingdom have adopted robotic assembly to improve manufacturing flexiblity. More than a half of users report no improvement in their ability to change production volume, and two-thirds claim no advantage in terms of product changeover. This is hardly surprising as more than 90 per cent of installations have replaced manual assembly rather than special-purpose automation. In some 80 per cent of cases robots simply augment special-purpose assembly automation, and robots perform the more complex assembly tasks. Nevertheless flexibility is important for the success of a significant proportion of users of the technology (Table 6.10).

Although many users describe their manufacturing processes as being highly varied or involving frequent changes, in practice one or two standard products typically account for 30–50 per cent of all production at any plant. These products tend to be assembled by robot, but other variants are still assembled by hand (Tidd, 1988a). As only a proportion of total production is assembled by robot, machine throughput is lower and therefore financial justification is more difficult: other things being equal, the higher the aggregate production volume, the easier justification becomes. But clearly the system must be sufficiently flexible. In the United Kingdom three-

Table 6.10 How users of robotic assembly in the UK describe their manufacturing processes

	% of plants
Low-volume, highly varied	16
Multiple products with frequent changes	23
Multiple products but with few changes	22
High volume, standardised product	39
Total	100

Source: Tidd, 1988a.

Table 6.11 Number of product variants assembled by robot in the UK, 1987

Number of variants	% Plants
1	13
2–5	34
6–9	27
10–24	20
25+	6
Total	100

Source: Tidd, 1988a.

quarters of users assemble less than ten different product variants by robot, and almost half less than five (Table 6.11).

Similarly only a third of users claim that robotic assembly has improved their ability to introduce new products. Over half of products assembled by robot have an anticipated life of more than five years, and over a third ten or more years (Table 6.12). Clearly robotic assembly is most commonly used for products with long life cycles. Assembly robots have an operational life of between five and seven years; therefore in most cases robotic assembly systems are written off over the life of the product, the same as special-purpose automation. This hardly encourages users to build flexibility into their robotic systems.

The volume flexibility of systems is also limited, and the time taken to implement robotic assembly makes capacity planning difficult. There are numerous examples of robotic assembly systems becoming unprofitable due to demand failing to reach estimates. In other cases demand has been higher than expected and additional capacity has been provided by employing additional workers. Many users of robotic assembly prefer to employ temporary workers to absorb unexpected or seasonal fluctuations in demand, rather than invest in additional productive capacity. As most have

Table 6.12 Anticipated life of products assembled by robot in the UK

Product life (years)	% Products assembled by robot (1987)	% All products (1989)
<1	7	3
1–3	13	12
3–5	23	30
5–9	20	36
10+	37	19
Total	100	100

Source: Tidd, 1988a; CBI, 1990.

just one or two robotic assembly cells an additional cell would require a significant increase in demand.

In short, there is little evidence in the United Kingdom of any form of 'low-cost flexible manufacturing' based on robotic assembly. In most cases the adoption of sophisticated robotics technology has been necessary to overcome organisational shortcomings, rather than to improve manufacturing flexibility.

7

Market pull: flexible manufacturing in Japan

Japan was the most successful manufacturing economy of the 1980s, and Japanese manufacturers made massive investments in all forms of programmable automation during that decade. It is tempting to link these two facts, but the precise relationship is unclear. Even after making allowances for differences in definitions, Japan has the highest density of industrial robots in the world and uses a larger proportion of its robots for assembly than any other country. This chapter examines the reasons for this and assesses the impact the technology has had on competitiveness.

7.1 The role of automation in Japan's success

The slogan *Wakon Yoshai*, 'Japanese spirit, Western technology‘, originates from the Meiji restoration. But as recently as the late 1950s the international competitiveness of most Japanese manufacturers was still based on low labour costs: the quality and performance of Japanese products was poor by international standards, and Japan competed on the basis of price. However, by the 1970s Japanese manufacturers were beginning to earn a reputation for high quality and had achieved international levels of productivity in key sectors such as the consumer electronics and automobile industries (Abernathy et al., 1981).

Over the same period the world's stereotype of a Japanese plant changed from that of a sweatshop full of low-paid but dedicated workers to a gleaming automated factory full of robots (Galjaard, 1981). Many other explanations for the success of Japanese manufacturers have been suggested, ranging from the macro to the micro: the 'incestuous' (*sic*) relationship between government and large manufacturers, so-called 'Japan Inc.' (Hayes & Wheelwright, 1984; Sethi et al., 1984); the unique organisational culture (Pascale & Athos, 1981); and manufacturing techniques (Schonberger, 1982). But massive investment in automation is one of the the most popular themes, and spawned the 'automate or liquidate' rhetoric of the 1980s.

However, Japanese manufacturers achieved their greatest improvements in productivity and quality before the widespread adoption of advanced manufacturing technology in Japan. During the 1960s productivity grew by an average of almost 9 per cent each year. In the 1970s this fell to around 5 per cent, and in the 1980s to nearer 3 per cent (OECD, 1988). Investment in programmable automation did not begin until the late 1970s, and 1980 is generally considered to be the 'first year of robotization' in Japan (Ishitani & Kaya, 1989; Watanabe, 1987). More detailed statistical analysis confirms that the widespread adoption of robots in Japan has had little impact on manufacturing productivity or output (Mori, 1989; Saito & Nakamura, 1989). Historically capital productivity in Japan has been similar to that in most other industrialised countries, but the productivity of labour has been higher (NEDC, 1985). This suggests that in the past work organisation and manufacturing techniques have been more important than investment in automation.

The experience of the Japanese automobile industry illustrates this. As early as 1965 the productivity at Toyota in Japan exceeded that of General Motors and Ford in the United States, but fixed assets — property, plant, and equipment — per vehicle were roughly comparable. By the early 1980s workers at Nissan and Toyota were more than twice as productive as their competitors in the United States and had more than double the fixed assets of their American counterparts, yet fixed assets per vehicle were similar (Cusumano, 1985). The growth in productivity slowed during the 1980s as NCMT and industrial robots began to be widely adopted, and in some cases productivity began to fall as model complexity and diversity increased (Table 7.1). A study of fifty-two automobile plants in Japan found that:

what is most important is that most NC machine tools and robots in the automobile industry were purchased in or after 1980, the year in which the highest hourly output per worker was reached in this industry. This implies that these new machines have not helped to save labour, or that their labour-saving effect has been more than offset by other factors . . . the main purpose of robotization in the Japanese automobile assembly can be summarized as (1) to increase flexibility of the production facilities, and (2) to solve or circumvent the problem of safety and health. (Watanabe, 1987, pp. 53–54)

To date Japanese manufacturers have been most successful in those sectors characterised by high-volume, standardised production, in particular consumer electronics and motor vehicles. Manufacturers of cars, motor cycles, audio and video equipment, cameras, and wrist-watches have pursued strategies based on high market share, and as a result have been able to make significant investments in special-purpose assembly automation. The number of assembly machines per worker, or density of machines, is more

Table 7.1 Vehicle productivity and robot density at Nissan and Toyota, 1980 and 1984

	Vehicle productivity[a]		Robot density[b]	
	1980	1984	1980	1984
Nissan	46.8	41.8	95.5	269.7
Toyota	61.3	58.4	56.5	221.4

[a]Annual production of vehicles per employee.
[b]Number of robots per 10,000 employees.
Source: Cusumano, 1985; Robot News, 1986.

Table 7.2 Distribution of special purpose assembly machines by industry in Japan, 1973–1987

	Number of machines			Density
	1973[a]	1981[a]	1987[b]	1987[c]
Electrical	2,632	14,123	28,295	164
Automobile	1,485	5,628	11,530	121
General machinery	1,830	2,578	4,499	34
Precision instruments	1,348	1,847	2,862	127
Other	325	771	780	9
Total	7,620	24,943	47,966	95

Source: Metalworking Engineering & Marketing, 1988a; ECE, 1988.
[a]Plants with 100 or more employees.
[b]Plants with 50 or more employees.
[c]Number of machines per 10,000 employees.

than ten times that in the United Kingdom (Table 7.2). Despite this, typically less than a third of all assembly operations were automated in 1983, and assembly still represented something of an automation 'bottleneck' (Tange, 1984). Consequently investment in more sophisticated forms of assembly automation increased significantly during the 1980s (Table 7.3).

7.2 Growth of robotic assembly

In 1980 only 16 per cent of machines produced in Japan were robots as defined in the West, but by 1986 more than half were; in terms of value the

Table 7.3 Production of industrial manipulators in Japan by type, 1980–1986

	Total annual production (% units)		
	1980	1983	1986
Tele-operators	10	3	1
Fixed-sequence manipulators	67	36	24
Variable-sequence manipulators	7	15	19
Playback robots	10	26	30
NC-robots	5	13	21
'Intelligent' robots	1	7	5
Total	100	100	100

Source: JIRA, 1987.

share of 'true' robots was over 80 per cent (JIRA, 1987). The trend away from convential special-purpose assembly automation towards robots has been greatest in the electronics/electrical industry. Fixed- and variable-sequence machines continued to be more popular in the automobile industry (Ishitani & Kaya, 1989). There are two possible reasons for this. The majority of assembly tasks in the automobile sector may be too complex for robotic assembly, whereas electronics assembly tends to be more straightforward. Alternatively manufacturers of consumer electronics may be demanding greater flexiblity as product diversity increases, and life cycles become shorter.

Probably the first and certainly the most publicised robotic assembly line in Japan was installed by Fanuc in 1982. At the showcase Fuji plant Fanuc manufactures servo-motors for NCMT and robots. In total around a hundred robots are used at the plant, about half in the machine shop for parts handling and machine loading, and half for assembly. Naturally Fanuc uses its own range of robots throughout the plant, but by Japanese standards these are relatively sophisticated and expensive devices. It is perhaps for this reason that Fanuc has been so successful exporting robots to the United States. The company has also formed joint ventures with both General Motors, and General Electric in the United States. However, in Japan simpler SCARA and Cartesian robots are much more commonplace.

Without a doubt the SCARA (Selective Compliance Robotic Assembly Arm) robot was the most significant development in the field of robotic assembly in Japan. The project began in 1978, the same year that Unimation launched its PUMA robot in the United States. But unlike the PUMA which was based on state-of-the-art technology, the SCARA was based on the needs of industry. Potential users of robotic assembly were involved in the SCARA project from the very beginning. In 1978 five Japanese firms agreed to cooperate, but by the time of the commercial launch of the robot in 1981, a total of thirteen Japanese firms had become

Table 7.4 Assembly as a proportion of all robot installations in Japan, 1980–1987*

	All robots ('000s)	Assembly robots ('000s)	%
1980	4.2	n.a.	n.a.
1981	9.7	0.6	6.9
1982	18.4	2.1	11.2
1983	32.4	4.8	14.8
1984	54.9	10.8	19.8
1985	83.1	18.2	21.9
1986	106.6	21.9	26.2
1987	121.5	n.a.	n.a.

*Excludes manual, fixed-, and variable-sequence manipulators.
Source: JIRA, 1987; Robot News, 1986.

involved. Most of these were not traditional machine-tool or robot manufacturers, but manufacturers of consumer durables: Hitachi, Sony, and Toshiba (consumer electronics); Yamaha Motors (motor cycles and engines); Seiko Instruments (clocks, watches); Pentel (pens); and Sankyo Seiki (musical box movements).

Research in the United States had indicated that about 60 per cent of parts were inserted into an assembly from a single direction, and a further 20 per cent from the opposite direction. In addition more than two-thirds of all assembly operations were simple 'peg-in-hole' fits or screwed together (Nevins & Whitney, 1978). In most cases design for automated assembly would further simplify assembly. Therefore an assembly robot would need only limited dexterity to perform most tasks, but would require some compliance (compliance is necessary to absorb positional errors and prevents jamming during assembly). The designers of the SCARA exploited these findings, and the result was an ingenious but relatively simple design using just two servo-motors. Nevertheless the SCARA is claimed to be suitable for up to 80 per cent of all assembly tasks, but typically costs only half as much as more 'versatile' machines like the PUMA (Hartley, 1984; Makino & Furuya, 1985).

It is difficult to overestimate the impact of the SCARA robot in Japan. Today there are more than twenty different manufacturers of assembly robots in Japan offering sixty different models, about half of which are based on the SCARA design (JIRA, 1988; Mortimer & Rooks, 1987). SCARA robots are available for applications as diverse as wrist-watch assembly and engine assembly. Since the launch of the SCARA family of robots in 1981 assembly applications have grown at about twice the rate of all other robot applications. By 1987 over a quarter of all robots used in Japan were for assembly (Table 7.4). This suggests that there are more than 30,000 'true' assembly robots in use in Japan today.

Table 7.5 Distribution of robotic assembly in Japan by sector and task

Industry	%	Task	%
Electrical*	52	PCB insertion	13
		Electro-mechanical	39
Automobile	37	Components	27
		Other	10
Precision mach.	11	Mechanical	11
Total	100		100

*Includes electrical and electronic automotive components.
Source: Makino & Yamafuji, 1988.

7.3 Patterns of adoption

It is relatively easy to identify reasons for the widespread adoption of robots in Japan, but far more difficult to determine which have been the most significant. An early study listed a host of contributive factors:

a burgeoning supply industry, the existence of strong automobile and electrical products industries, high capital investment in manufacturing plant, generally favourable labour relations, incipient skilled labour shortages, and a coherent policy of state support. (White, 1983)

The rapid growth of the Japanese automobile industry during the 1970s clearly played a major role in the diffusion of industrial robots, in particular in process applications such as spot-welding and painting. The electronics/ electrical sector provided a similar stimulus to robotic assembly in the 1980s, to both the supply and demand side. This sector currently accounts for more than half of all assembly robots in Japan (Table 7.5).

Improvements to automatic parts insertion machines allow many odd-form electronic components to be inserted into printed circuit boards (pcbs), and assembly robots are most commonly used for more complex electro-mechanical assembly. In particular manufacturers of consumer electronics such as televisions, video cassette recorders (VCRs), and video cameras have made extensive use of robotic assembly. Typically such manufacturers have a wide product range with short life cycles, produced in high aggregate volumes. In such circumstances flexiblity is essential, and robotics technology is relatively easy to justify financially. Japanese manufacturers pay a great deal of attention to product design in order to reduce the need for sophisticated robotics technology. The main purpose of robotics is to improve flexibility.

Hitachi's VCR plant is a good example of this approach. In 1981 the product consisted of 460 discrete mechanical, electrical, and electronic parts. Electronics assembly was fully automated, but the remaining mechanical and electrical parts were assembled by hand. The 1983 design had 370 parts which were assembled by a combination of 11 SCARA robots, 52 special-purpose (pick-and-place) machines, and 9 workers. The 1985 model had just 250 parts, and was assembled by 24 robots and 71 special-purpose machines. As a result the number of operations automated has increased from 86 per cent to 98 per cent, but at the same time the number of variants assembled increased to eighteen.

Similarly manufacturers of automotive components have also made significant investments in robotic assembly. Over a quarter of all assembly robots in Japan are used by manufacturers of automotive components, and even a greater proportion if manufacturers of electrical and electronic components are included. Significantly robots appear to have replaced special-purpose machines in this sector, which suggests flexibility may be a major factor. One of the largest component suppliers, Nippondenso, has responded to shorter life cycles and wider product ranges by replacing special-purpose assembly machines with programmable robots (Hartley, 1984). A survey of automobile plants in Japan found that more than half of the robots had replaced or substituted for special-purpose automation, rather than labour (Watanabe, 1987). The most recent application of robotics in the automobile industry has been in final assembly.

Since 1985 Nissan has used robots to install the battery, window glass, seats, rear door, lamps, and spare wheel at its showcase Zama plant, and plans to automate half of all final assembly operations when its new model range is introduced (Bairstow, 1986). Honda is planning to integrate the existing 150 assembly operations into just fifty, and to use robots to perform 80 per cent of these (*Japan Economic Journal*, December 1986). Japanese automobile companies have followed a more consistent approach to adoption of robotic assembly than their American or European competitors. Three-quarters of all automobile plants in Japan have automated battery insertion, almost two-thirds windscreen and rear screen insertion, and half the insertion of the spare wheel (Krafcik, 1989). In the United States and Europe much higher levels of assembly automation have been achieved in a handful of showcase plants, but in general levels are lower than in Japan. A study of eighty automobile plants in fifteen countries concluded that 'while Western plants lag in the introduction of simple automation applications, they are on a par with or ahead of their Japanese counterparts in automating complex processes requiring substantial investments in specialized equipment' (Krafcik, 1989, p. 10).

The adoption of robotic assembly in Japan has been consistent across all sectors, but as in the United Kingdom the technology has been most successful in larger plants. Robotic assembly is most common in plants having more than 300 employees in all industries (Table 7.6). The Japanese government has introduced several schemes to promote the use of robots by

Table 7.6 Distribution of robotic assembly in Japan by plant size & industry

| Industry | Density of assembly robots* | | | | |
| | Plant size (no. of employees) | | | | |
	<100	100–299	300–999	1,000+	All
Electrical	0	65	199	185	97
Automobile	18	0	208	157	107
Precision engineering	0	121	212	218	94
All manufacturing	1	17	67	91	23

*Number of assembly robot per 10,000 employees.
Source: Tange, 1984; Statistics Bureau Japan, 1985; Yamafuji & Makino, 1987.

Table 7.7 Annual production of products assembled by robot in Japan

Annual production volume*	% Products assembled by robot
<250,000	2.7
250,000–500,000	9.3
500,000–1 million	33.3
1–2.5 million	37.3
2.5–5 million	13.3
5 million+	4.0
Total	100.0

*Calculated from cycle time assuming two-shift operation.
Source: Makino & Yamafuji, 1988; Tange, 1984.

smaller manufacturers, such as the Japan Robot Leasing Company and Small Business Finance Corporation (Baranson, 1983; Yonemoto, 1987), but these have had little impact. A review of government support found that over a third of small to medium sized users of robots in Japan failed to achieve their production goals (Tanaka, 1986).

Cost is one reason for this size bias. In Japan an assembly robot will typically cost much more than the annual wages of an assembly worker, and two to three times as much as a special-purpose, pick-and-place machine. Contrary to widespread belief, most firms in Japan are not willing to accept longer payback periods than their counterparts in the West; many require payback within a single man-year (Ishitani & Kaya, 1989). Consequently robotic assembly can only be justified for relatively high-volume, albeit flexible manufacturing (Table 7.7).

Table 7.8 Role of assembly-line operators in Japan

Task	Percentage of operators' time
Product assembly	22.1
Parts supply	21.7
Quality inspection	17.4
Machine monitoring	14.5
Routine maintenance	12.9
Recording data	7.3
Other duties	4.1
Total	100.0

Source: Tange, 1984; Yamafuji & Makino, 1987.

7.4 Organisational issues

Contrary to the popular image of a Japanese factory, few are fully automated or can run unmanned. In fact robotic assembly systems in Japan rely on operator involvement; as Makino, inventor of the SCARA robot, notes: 'much of the automation in Japanese assembly lines is simple and relies heavily on co-operation from the operators to keep it going' (quoted in Hartley, 1984, p. 106). Consequently users place greater emphasis on training than most of their counterparts in the West: over 80 per cent of the plants using robotic assembly have training programmes for operators (Yamafuji & Makino, 1987). An operator in Japan will normally be responsible for between five and ten robot stations on a line, and is expected to clear machine blockages, monitor assembly quality, carry out routine maintenance, as well as supply parts and carry out some assembly work (Table 7.8).

It has been argued that technological systems in Japan are so highly linked to existing organisational structures and processes that firms are ill equipped to deal with diversity or change (Kagono *et al.*, 1985). However, continued reliance on multi-skilled operatives and commitment to quality and design has allowed Japanese manufacturers to adopt less complex technology and thus improve flexibility. This is the principle behind socio-technical theory: optimisation of either work organisation or production technology is unlikely to result in an optimum system; joint optimisation of organisation and technology may therefore require a less than optimum state in each element (Trist *et al.*, 1963). Significantly many of the socio-technical experiments of the 1960s resulted in systems similar to current Japanese practice (Tidd, 1986).

Table 7.9 Type of industrial robot used for assembly in Japan

Robot configuration	% Assembly robots
SCARA	47.3
Cartesian	40.2
Cylindrical	7.9
Articulated	3.5
Other	1.1
Total	100.0

Source: Makino & Yamafuji, 1988.

7.5 Technological trajectories

As noted earlier, during the 1980s investment in 'true' robots grew much faster than in fixed- and variable-sequence devices. Nonetheless users in Japan still favour less sophisticated robots than their counterparts in the West. Almost half of all assembly robots in use in Japan are of the SCARA type, and a further 40 per cent are simple Cartesian machines (Table 7.9). This is possible for two reasons: firstly, almost 90 per cent of all assembly robots in Japan are used in multi-robot assembly lines rather than in cells, and therefore require less dexterity (Chapter 5); and secondly, attention to organisational issues.

Toyota's approach to automation illustrates this. At Toyota *jidoka* or 'intelligent automation' has a very different meaning than in the West. It does not refer to the application of Artificial Intelligence (AI) techniques to industrial automation, but rather to the simplification of operations for workers in order to minimise operator error (Mikazaki *et al.*, 1988). All assembly automation at Toyota must satisfy the following 'Ten Commandments':

1. Equipment must be safe and easy to start and stop;
2. Defects should be detected and corrected at source and not passed to the next process;
3. Production should be pulled from previous process, not pushed by forced conveyance;
4. Common operations from different lines should not be combined, but each line balanced independently to maximise production flexibility;
5. Automation should begin with operations at the end of the production process, not those easiest to automate;
6. All equipment must be easy to back up in the event of breakdown;
7. Cost of equipment, including allowance for the space taken up, should be proportional to value-added;
8. All equipment should stand alone, be easy to relocate and have variable speed to cope with changes in production;

9. All equipment must have the flexibility to cope with model and equipment changes, and therefore modular in addition to programmable;
10. The production line is not a laboratory, and therefore new unproven technology should be avoided. (Miyazaki *et al.*, 1988)

7.6 Impact on flexibility

Traditionally the Japanese have been strongest at high-volume, repetitive manufacturing (Schonberger, 1982). Japanese manufacturers use more robots than their American and European competitors, but these robots tend to be less sophisticated. Consequently many observers in the West believe that systems in Japan are not as flexible as those in Europe and the United States, but this is not the case.

The ability to manufacture a large product mix at a single plant has become increasingly important in Japan. One survey revealed that the number of product variants manufactured increased by a fifth between 1981 and 1985, and a quarter of plants had increased their product range by between 20–50 per cent (Economic Research Institute, 1985). This trend has been most dramatic in the consumer durables sector. For example, in 1980 Nissan offered 16 different models and 36 body styles; in 1988 the options had increased to 24 and 50 respectively (Yamauchi, 1988).

But programmable automation has not been the driving force behind the trend towards greater product diversity. This has largely been market-led. Robotics and other advanced manufacturing technologies have allowed manufacturers in Japan to overcome the traditional trade-off between efficiency and flexibility, the so-called 'productivity dilemma'. For example, in the early 1980s Seiko was threatened by the introduction of cheap electronic wrist-watches. The company responded by redesigning its range of analogue watches and investing in appropriate assembly: watch movements are assembled by special-purpose pick-and-place machines as there are few variants; but robots are used for the case assembly, which involves fitting the glass, face, hands, and movement into the case. As a result Seiko can offer a wider range of products at lower prices. and the company now dominates the world market. Almost half of all robotic assembly systems in Japan produce more than ten product variants (Table 7.10).

In addition product life cycles in Japan are becoming shorter in many industries. In 1981, 78 per cent of products manufactured in Japan had life cycles of more than three years, but by 1985 the proportion had fallen to 53 per cent (Economic Research Institute, 1985). This trend reflects Japanese manufacturers commitment to continuous product development (Imai *et al.*, 1985), rather than the potential of programmable automation. Nevertheless a third of products assembled by robot have life cycles of three years or less, and almost two-thirds of five years or less (Table 7.11).

The electronics sector is the best example. Sony's robotic assembly line

Table 7.10 Number of product styles assembled by robot in Japan

Number of product variants	% Robot installations
1–2	16.4
3–5	25.5
6–10	12.7
11–20	12.7
21–50	18.2
51–100	3.6
101+	10.9
Total	100.0

Source: Makino & Yamafuji, 1988.

Table 7.11 Life cycle of products assembled by robot in Japan, by sector

Product life (years)	% robot installations				
	Electrical	Automotive	Machinery	Precision instruments	All
<0.5	3	0	8	0	3
0.5–1	8	0	0	20	4
1–3	34	25	8	20	26
3–5	24	38	38	40	31
5+	34	38	46	20	36
Total	100	100	100	100	100

Source: Tange, 1984; Yamafuji & Makino, 1987.

for the 'Super Walkman' accommodated three model changes in the first eighteen months of production, and took under a week to retool and change over in each case. Like many other consumer electronics companies in Japan, Sony is both a supplier and user of assembly robots. The company also uses robots to assemble other rapidly changing product lines, such as the 8mm video camera. However, there is little evidence that robotic assembly systems in Japan can easily accommodate significant changes in production volume. The ability to change product mix allows users to cope with small fluctuations in demand, but multi-robot assembly lines are inherently more difficult to expand in a modular fashion. In some hybrid systems, in which each robot station performs several operations, additional robot stations can be added subject to line balancing requirements. In practice many users in Japan design the capacity of the robot line to be less than the anticipated level of demand, and when necessary use their workforce and subsidiary firms for additional capacity.

In short, Japanese manufacturers of a wide range of consumer durables are pursuing a strategy of high-volume, flexible production. Through extensive investment in relatively simple robotics technology, users have been able to increase their product ranges and reduce product life cycles without the traditional cost penalty.

8

Manufacturing strategy and technological divergence

The experience of users suggests that organisational context has a significant effect on the development and implementation of advanced manufacturing technologies. This final chapter contrasts trends in Japan and the West and assesses the implications for international competitiveness.

8.1 Technological divergence

Numerous studies have examined the impact of advanced manufacturing technologies on firms, but have failed to identify any dominant pattern of adoption or international 'best practice'. The development and subsequent diffusion of numerically controlled machine tools (NCMT), flexible machining systems (FMS), and industrial robots have followed different paths in different countries. In particular, the approach of Japanese suppliers and users of these technologies contrasts with that of their counterparts in the West.

American and, to a lesser extent, European suppliers of NCMT, FMS and robots have focused on expensive, sophisticated technology suitable for a limited range of specialist applications. In contrast Japanese suppliers, who are frequently users too, have developed less complex technologies suitable for a much wider range of applications. Patterns of adoption are also different. In the United States and Europe NCMT have had the greatest impact in small to medium-sized plants where they have replaced groups of conventional machine tools; FMS have subsequently replaced groups of NCMT in larger plants. In Japan NCMT and FMS have often also replaced special-purpose transfer systems. Several studies have found that FMS in the United States and Europe are not being managed for flexibility, compared to systems in Japan.

The development and adoption of industrial robots is another example of divergence. The robot was originally conceived in the 1960s as a 'universal'

Table 8.1 Typical characteristics of robotic assembly systems in the UK and Japan

	UK	Japan
Number of robots	3	15
Most common type of robot	Articulated	SCARA
System configuration	Cell	Line
Annual production volume	250,000	1,000,000
Number of product variants	6	15
Product life cycle (years)	7	4

Source: Tidd, 1988d.

form of automation or 'steel collar' worker, but has since become increasingly task-specific: specialised welding robots, painting robots, and assembly robots are now commonplace. Historically the automobile industry has been the largest user of robots, and has had a significant influence on the development of early handling and process robots. More recently the electrical sector has played a similar role in the development of assembly robots. Assembly has traditionally been labour-intensive and represented an automation bottleneck. Many commentators predicted that the availability of assembly robots would result in the widespread automation of assembly during the 1980s, but this has failed to occur.

British industry has a lower density of robots than all its major competitors, and uses a smaller proportion of these robots for assembly. Japanese industry has the highest robot density in the world, and uses the largest proportion for assembly. But the most significant differences are qualitative rather than quantitative. In the United Kingdom a robotic assembly system typically consists of two or three robotic assembly cells based on relatively sophisticated articulated robots and incorporates sensor technology. In Japan multi-robot assembly lines based on much simpler SCARA and Cartesian robots are more commonplace. Despite this, Japanese systems are more flexible than those in British companies: more product variants are assembled and product life cycles are shorter (Table 8.1).

Clearly technology has not been the most significant factor. In both the United Kingdom and Japan organisational context has strongly influenced the development and adoption of the technology, which in turn has affected manufacturing flexibility. In the United Kingdom operators receive little training and are low skilled. Communication between design, manufacturing, sales, suppliers and customers is poor and consequently products are frequently not designed for ease of manufacture, and components are of uncertain quality. Relatively advanced, complex manufacturing technology is necessary to overcome such constraints. This is typically difficult to justify and implement, and system complexity reduces flexibility. In Japan users have the advantage of a highly trained, multi-skilled work-force, good communication between different functions, and close relationships with suppliers. Design for manufacture and high-quality components are the norm. Consequently the manufacturing technology need not be as sophisticated, and financial justification is easier. The reduction in system complexity and use of skilled operators also increases the flexibility.

In most cases manufacturers in the West have adopted AMT as a 'technological fix' for what are essentially organisational shortcomings in order to match Japanese levels of productivity and quality. But this strategy is unlikely to succeed if organisational context has such a profound effect on the successful implementation of such technologies. Users must first tackle organisational problems. Japanese manufacturers have achieved such high levels of productivity and quality through the widespread adoption of total quality management, just-in-time production techniques, and so-called 'lean' production systems (Krafcik & MacDuffie, 1989). They are now building on this success and are making substantial investments in programmable manufacturing technologies in order to achieve flexible, but low-cost production. In short, both organisational context and market strategy have influenced technological trajectories (Table 8.2).

8.2 Strategic implications

In successful companies manufacturing systems are consistent with corporate strategy. There is a growing awareness of the need to consider the manufacturing implications of corporate strategy, in particular the demands marketing requirements place on production priorities. Any production system will involve some trade-offs and compromises, and one of the most fundamental has traditionally been that between efficiency and flexibility. Increases in automation have been associated with a reduction in flexibility — the so-called 'productivity dilemma' (Abernathy, 1978). During the 1970s there was a growing mismatch between marketing requirements and manufacturing capabilities. Faced with more intense international competition and declining demand, many manufacturers responded by increasing their product range and the number of options within each range. This satisfied marketing requirements, but significantly increased the cost and complexity of manufacturing systems (Hill, 1980).

Companies have responded to this dilemma in two very different ways. The first approach, which originated in the United States but is now also popular in Europe, has been to reduce product diversity and thus the complexity of production processes. American and many European automobile manufacturers have consistently reduced model ranges and product options in order to facilitate automation and reduce costs (Cusumano, 1985; Krafcik, 1988b), and there has been a more general

Table 8.2 Factors influencing the development and adoption of flexible manufacturing technologies in Japan and the West

	Europe and US	Japan
Organisational context	Poorly trained, low-skilled operators; little communication between design, manufacturing, and sales functions; distant relationship with suppliers and customers; 'robust' production systems	Highly trained, multi-skilled operators; good communication between design, manufacturing, and sales functions; close relationship between suppliers and customers; 'lean' production systems
Source of most significant developments	Specialist suppliers, essentially 'technology push'	Major users, essentially 'demand pull'
Primary motives for development and adoption	To increase productivity and improve quality through the elimination of direct labour	To improve flexibility of production but continue to reduce costs through the elimination of waste
Technological trajectory pursued	Complex, sophisticated technology consistent with long-term goal of CIM; essentially a 'computer systems' approach	Relatively simple, proven technology with continued reliance on operators; essentially a 'production engineering' approach
Manufacturing strategy	Reduction in diversity of production to facilitate further automation and computer integration	Flexible, but low-cost production

trend towards more specialised, focused factories (Skinner, 1985). Ironically this has been strongest in those sectors most susceptible to changing consumer tastes: 'companies, including manufacturers of appliances, autos, copiers, and cameras are following this approach of simplifying and focusing product offerings' (Schonberger, 1987, p. 97).

The other response, characteristic of Japanese manufacturers, has been to improve the flexibility of production systems to cope with the new market demands. The Japanese have concentrated on developing the capability to offer a high variety of products with shorter life cycles without increasing costs, while manufacturers in the West have been preoccupied with matching the Japanese in terms of quality and productivity (Ferdows *et al*, 1986). Japanese manufacturers successfully overcame the traditional trade-off between cost and quality in the 1970s, and there is overwhelming evidence that they will challenge the trade-off between efficiency and flexibility during the 1990s. But the widespread adoption of flexible manufacturing technologies is a necessary but not a sufficient condition for success. American and European manufacturers are banking on computer-integrated 'smart' factories to achieve Japanese levels of productivity and quality, but may find themselves ill-equipped to compete with low-cost flexible production. The competitiveness of AMT will ultimately depend on organisational issues and market strategy, rather than smarter technology.

Bibliography

Abernathy, W. J. (1978) *The Productivity Dilemma: Roadblock to Innovation in the Automobile Industry*, Baltimore, Johns Hopkins University Press.

Abernathy, W. J., Clark, K. B., & Kantrow, A. M. (1981) 'The New Industrial Competition', *Harvard Business Review*, September/October, pp. 68–81.

——(1983) *Industrial Renaissance*, New York, Basic Books.

Abraham, R. G. (1977) 'Programmable Automation of Batch Assembly Operations', *The Industrial Robot*, No. 3, Vol. 4, pp. 119–31.

ACARD (1979) *Joining and Assembly: The Impact of Robots and Automation*, London, HMSO.

ACAS (1987) *Labour Flexibility in Britain: The 1987 ACAS Survey*, London, ACAS.

Acs, Z. J., Audretsch, D. B. & Carlsson, B. (1988) *Flexible Technology and Firm Size*, Berlin, International Institute of Management, Wissenschaftszentrum Berlin Sozialforschung.

Aglietta, M. (1979) *A Theory of Capitalist Regulation: The US Experience*, London, New Left Books.

Allen, P.M. (1988) 'Evolution, Innovation and Economics', Dosi, G. *et al.* (eds) *Technical Change & Economic Theory*, London, Pinter, pp. 95–119.

Altshuler, A., Anderson, M., Jones, D. T., Roos, D., & Womack, J. (1985) *The Future of the Automobile*, London, Unwin.

American Machinist (1983) *The 13th American Machinist Inventory of Metalworking Equipment*, New York, McGraw-Hill.

——(1989) 'The 14th Inventory of Metalworking Equipment', *American Machinist*, November, Special Report 808.

Appleton, E. & Williams, D. J. (1987) *Industrial Robot Applications*, Milton Keynes, Open University Press.

Arai, T. (1988) 'A Model of Automization on a Final Assembly Line in the Automobile Industry', *Assembly Automation: Japan vs Europe Forum*, Bedford, IFS, pp. 25–36.

Arcangeli, F., Dosi, G., & Moggi, M. (1987) *Patterns of Diffusion of Electronics Technology*, Brighton, DRC Discussion Paper, SPRU, University of Sussex.

Arnold, E. (1983) 'Information Technology as a Technological Fix: Computer Aided Design in the UK', in Winch, G. (ed.) *Information Technology in Manufacturing Processes*, London, Rossendale, pp. 31–43.

Association Française de Robotique Industrielle (AFRI) (1988) *Statistiques 1988*, Paris (in French).

Atkinson, J. (1984) *Flexibility, Uncertainty and Manpower Management*, Brighton, Institute of Manpower Studies, Report No. 89.

——(1985) 'Flexibility: Planning for an Uncertain Future', *Manpower Policy and Practice*, Summer, Vol. 1, pp. 26–9.

Atkinson, J. & Meager, N. (1986) *New Forms of Work Organisation*, Brighton, Institute of Manpower Studies, Report No. 121.

Ayres, R.U. & Miller, S. (1981) 'Robotics, CAM, and Industrial Productivity', *National Productivity Review*, Winter 1981/82, pp. 42–60.

——(1983) *Robotics: Applications and Social Implications*, Cambridge, Mass., Ballinger.

——(1985) *Robotics and Flexible Manufacturing Technologies: Assessment, Impacts, and Forecasts*, New Jersey, Noyes.

Bairstow, J. (1986) 'Automated Automaking', *High Technology* (Boston), No. 8, Vol. 6, pp. 25–8.

Baranson, J. (1983) *Robots in Manufacturing: Key to International Competitiveness*, Maryland, Lomond.

Bell, R. M. (1972) *Changing Technology and Manpower Requirements in the Engineering Industry*, Brighton, Sussex University Press & EITB.

Bernt, J. (1986) 'Flexible Assembly Robots: The Bosch Approach', *Assembly Automation*, Vol.6, No. 2, pp. 77–80.

Bessant, J. (1983) 'Management and Manufacturing Innovation: the Case of Information Technology', in Winch, G. (ed.) *Information Technology in Manufacturing Processes*, London, Rossendale, pp. 14–30.

——(1988) 'Pushing Boxes or Solving Problems? Some Marketing Issues in the Diffusion of Computer-Integrated Manufacturing Innovations', *Journal of Marketing Management*, Vol.3, No.3, pp. 352–71.

Bessant, J. & Haywood, B. (1985) *The Introduction of Flexible Manufacturing Systems as an Example of Computer Integrated Manufacturing*, Brighton, Brighton Business School.

Björkman, M. and Ekdahl, B. (1988) 'Computer Model for Economic Justification of Industrial Robot Installations', in Jarvis, R. A. (ed.) *Proceedings of the International Symposium and Exposition on Robots*, Bedford, IFS, pp. 868–74.

Blackburn, P., Coombs, R., & Green, K. (1985) *Technology, Economic Growth and the Labour Process*, London, Macmillan.

Boothroyd, G. (1980) *Design for Assembly: A Designer's Handbook*, University of Massachusetts.

——(1985) 'Economics of General Purpose Robotic Assembly', in Rathmill, K. (ed.) *Robotic Assembly*, Bedford, IFS, pp. 335–46.

Boothroyd, G. & Dewhurst, P. (1983) *Design for Assembly: A Designer's Handbook*, Amherst, Mass., MIT Press.

Boothroyd, G. & Redford, A. H. (1968) *Mechanised Assembly*, London, McGraw-Hill.

Boyer, R. (1988) 'Technical Change and the Theory of "Regulation"', Dosi, G. *et al.* (eds.) *Technical Change and Economic Theory*, London, Pinter, pp. 67–94.

Bright, J. R. (1958) *Automation and Management*, Cambridge, Mass., Harvard University Press.

British Robot Association (BRA) (1981) *Robot Facts*, Bedford, BRA.

——(1984) *Robot Facts*, Bedford, BRA.

——(1986) *Robot Facts*, Bedford, BRA.

——(1988) *Robot Facts*, Birmingham, BRA.

——(1989) *Robot Facts*, Birmingham, BRA.

Browne, J., Rathmill, K., Sethi, S. P. & Stecke, K. E. (1984) 'Classification of Flexibile Manufacturing Systems', *The FMS Magazine*, April, pp. 114–17.

Buchanan, D. A. (1986) *Canned Cycles and Dancing Tools: Who's Really in Control of Computer-Aided Machining?*, Glasgow, Working Paper No.1, Department of Management Studies, Glasgow University.

Buchanan, D. A. & Boddy, D. (1983) *Organisations in the Computer Age: Technological Imperatives and Strategic Choice*, London, Gower.

Burbridge, J. L. (1978) 'Whatever Happened to GT?', *Management Today*, September.

Burton, J. & Ford, F. (1985) 'What Goes Wrong on the Assembly Floor', *Proceedings of the 6th International Conference on Assembly Automation*, Bedford, IFS, pp. 217–20.

Buzacott, J. A. (1982) 'The Fundamental Principles of Flexibility in Manufacturing Systems', *Proceedings of the 1st International Conference on Flexible Manufacturing Systems*, Bedford, IFS, pp. 13–21.

CBI (1990) *Innovation Trends Survey Results 1989*, London, CBI.

Central Statistics Office (CSO) (1988) Annual Abstract of Statistics, HMSO, London.

Cimoli, M. & Dosi, G. (1986) *Technology and Development: Some Implications in the Economics of Innovation for the Process of Development*, DRC Discussion Paper No. 35, Brighton, SPRU, University of Sussex.

Clarke, K. (1989) 'Persuasive Accounting', *Manufacturing Engineer*, June, pp. 59–61

Cole, R. E. & Yakushiji, T. (1984) *The American and Japanese Auto Industries in Transition*, Tokyo, Technova.

Conigliaro, L. (1983) 'Trends in the Robot Industry (Revisited)', in *Proceedings of the 13th International Symposium on Industrial Robots*, Amsterdam, North Holland.

Connock, S. (1985) 'Workforce Flexibility', *Personnel Management*, October, pp. 36–8.

Constant, E. W. (1980) *The Origins of the Turbojet Revolution*, Baltimore, Johns Hopkins University Press.

Coombs, R. W. (1984) 'Long-term Trends in Automation', Marstrand, P. (ed.) *New Technology and the Future of Work & Skills*, London, Pinter.

Coombs, R. W, Saviotti, P., & Walsh, V. (1987) *Economics and Technological Change*, Basingstoke, Macmillan.

Csakvary, T. (1981) 'Product Selection Procedure for Programmable Automatic Assembly', *Proceedings of the 2nd International Conference on Assembly Automation*, Bedford, IFS, pp. 201–10.

Cusumano, M. A. (1985) *The Japanese Automobile Industry: Technology and Management at Nissan and Toyota*, Cambridge, Mass., Harvard University Press.

Dale, E. & Michelon, L. C. (1986) *Modern Management Methods*, Middlesex, Penguin Edition.

Dataquest (1988) *Worldwide Industrial Robots Market Forecast*, Orlando, Fla., Dataquest.

Dempsey, P. (1983) 'New Corporate Perspectives in FMS', in Rathmill, K. (ed.) *Proceedings of the 2nd International Conference on Flexible Manufacturing Systems*, Bedford, IFS.

Diebold, J. (1952) *Automation: The Advent of the Automatic Factory*, New York, Van Nostran.

Dodd, G. G. (1988) 'Artificial Intelligence for Flexible Manufacturing: An Assessment', in Jarvis. R.A. (ed.) *Proceedings of the International Symposium and Exposition on Robots*, Bedford, IFS, pp. 131–48.

Dore, R. P. (1973) *British Factory, Japanese Factory*, London, Allen & Unwin.

——(1986) *Flexible Rigidities: Industrial Policy & Structural Adjustment in the Japanese Economy 1970–80*, London, Athelone Press.

——(1987) *Taking Japan Seriously: A Confucian Perspective on Leading Economic Issues*, London, Athelone Press.

Dosi, G (1982) 'Technological Paradigms and Technological Trajectories', *Research Policy*, Vol. 11, No. 3, pp. 147–62.

——(1986) *Sources and Microeconomic Effects of Innovation*, Brighton, DRC Discussion Paper, SPRU, University of Sussex.

——(1988) 'The Nature of the Innovative Process', in Dosi, G., Freeman, C., Nelson, R., Silverberg, G., & Soete, L. (eds) *Technical Change and Economic Theory*, London, Pinter, pp. 221–38.

Dosi, G., Freeman, C., Nelson, R., Silverberg, G., & Soete, L. (1988) *Technical Change and Economic Theory*, London, Pinter.

Dunlop, L. F. (1983) 'Management and Robots: An Investigation of the Nature and Significance to Management of Assembly Robot Flexibility', M.Phil. thesis, Oxford Centre for Management Studies, University of Oxford.

Economic Commission for Europe (ECE) (1985) *Production and Use of Industrial Robots*, New York, United Nations.
——(1986) *Recent Trends in Flexible Manufacturing*, New York, United Nations.
——(1988) *Annual Review of Engineering Industries and Automation 1986*, New York, United Nations.
Economic Research Institute (1985) *Evolution and Future Problems of Factory Automation*, Tokyo, Japan Society for the Promotion of the Machine Tool Industry (in Japanese).
——(1987) *Present State and Future Trends in CAD and CIM*, Tokyo, Japan Society for the Promotion of the Machine Tool Industry (in Japanese).
Edquist, C. & Jacobsson, S. (1988) *Flexible Automation: The Global Diffusion of New Technology in the Engineering Industry*, Oxford, Basil Blackwell.
Engelberger, J. L. (1980) *Robots in Practice: Management and Applications of Industrial Robots*, London, Kogan Page.
Engineering Industry Training Board (1988) *Economic Indicators*, No. 28, Watford, EITB.
Ergas, H. (1984) 'Corporate Strategies in Transition', in Jacquemin, A. (ed.) *European Industry: Public Policy & Corporate Strategy*, Oxford, Clarendon Press.
Fabrizi, D. (1988) 'L'Industria ed il Mercato della Robotica in Italia', *Tecniche dell'Automazione*, pp. 50–64 (in Italian)
Fallon, I. & Srodes, J. (1988) *Takeovers*, London, Pan Books.
Ferdows, K., Miller, J. G., Nakane, J., & Vollmann, T. E. (1986) 'Evolving Global Manufacturing Strategies: Projections into the 1990s', *International Journal of Operation and Production Management*, Vol. 6, No. 4, pp. 6–16.
Ferguson, C. H. (1988) 'From the People Who Brought You Voodoo Economics', *Harvard Business Review*, Vol. 88, No. 3, pp. 55–62.
Ferguson, N. C. (1978) 'A History of Numerically Controlled Machine Tools', *CME*, September, pp. 89–92.
Fiat Auto S.p.A. (1987) *Factory Automation Statistics*, Milan, Fiat.
Fix-Stertz, J., Lay, G., Schultz-Wild, R., & Wengel, J. (1987) *Flexible Manufacturing Systems and Cells in the Scope of New Production Systems in Germany*, Munich, FAST Occasional Paper.
Fleck, J. (1983) 'Robots in Manufacturing Organisations', in Winch, G. (ed.) *Information Technology in Manufacturing Processes*, London, Rossendale.
——(1987a) *Innofusion or Diffusion? The Nature of Technological Development in Robotics*, University of Edinburgh, Dept. of Business Studies, Working Paper 87/9.
——(1987b) *Robotics: Organisation and Management*, University of Edinburgh, Dept. of Business Studies, Working Paper 87/13.

Fleck, J. & White, B. (1984) 'National Policies and Patterns of Diffusion', *Proceedings of the 14th International Symposium on Industrial Robots*, Bedford, IFS, pp. 13–23.

Ford, H., & Crowther, S. (1924) *My Life and Work*, London, Heinemann.

Foyer, P. & Drazan, P. (1986) 'Assembly: The Cinderella of Factories', *Production Engineer*, March, pp. 41–2.

Freeman, C. & Perez, C. (1988) 'Structural Crises of Adjustment, Business Cycles and Business Behaviour' in Dosi, G., Freeman, C., Nelson, R., Silverberg, G., & Soete, L. (eds) *Technical Change and Economic Theory*, London, Pinter, pp. 38–66.

Galjaard, J. H. (1981) *A Technology Based Nation: An Inquiry into Industrial Organisation and Robotizing in Japan*, Delft, Netherlands, Interuniversity Institute of Management.

Gardiner, J. P. (1984) 'Design Trajectories for Airplanes and Automobiles', in Freeman, C. (ed.) *Design Innovation and Long Cycles in Economic Development*, London, Royal College of Art, pp. 185–214.

Georghiou, L., Metcalfe, J. S., Gibbons, M., Ray, T., & Evans, J. (1986) *Post-Innovation Performance*, Basingstoke, Macmillan.

Gerwin, D. (1982) 'Do's and don'ts of Computerised Manufacturing', *Harvard Business Review*, March–April, pp. 107–16.

Goldhar, J. D. & Jelinek, M. (1983) 'Plan for Economies of Scope', *Harvard Business Review*, Vol. 61, No. 6, pp. 141–8.

Gorz, A. (1982) *Farewell to the Working Class*, London, Pluto Press.

——(1985) *Paths to Paradise*, London, Pluto Press.

Gustavsson, S. (1985) 'Flexibility and Productivity in Complex Manufacturing Processes', in Raouf, A. & Ahmad, S.I. (eds) *Flexible Manufacturing: Recent Developments in FMS, Robotics, CAD/CAM, CIM*, Amsterdam, Elsevier, pp. 153–62.

Hartley, J. (1984) *Flexible Automation in Japan*, Bedford, IFS.

——(1985) 'Flexible Factories: Do They Work?', *The Engineer*, April, pp. 52–4.

Hayes, R. H. & Wheelwright, S. C. (1979), 'Link Manufacturing Process and Product Life Cycles', *Harvard Business Review*, Jan.–Feb., pp. 133–40.

Hayes, R.H. & Jaikumar, R. (1988) 'Manufacturing Crisis: New Technologies, Obsolete Organisations', *Harvard Business Review*, Vol. 88, No. 5, pp. 77–85.

Hayes, R. H. & Wheelwright, S. C. (1984) *Restoring Our Competitive Edge: Competing Through Manufacturing*, New York, Wiley & Sons.

Haywood, B. & Bessant, J. (1987a) *FMS and the Small to Medium Sized Firm*, Brighton, Innovation Research Group, Brighton Polytechnic.

Haywood, B. & Bessant, J. (1987b) *The Swedish Approach to the Use of Flexible Manufacturing Systems*, Brighton, Innovation Research Group, Brighton Polytechnic.

Heginbotham, W, B. (1984) *Programmable Assembly*, Bedford, IFS.

Hickson, D. J. & MacMillan, C. J. (1981) *Organisation and Nation: The Aston Programme IV*, London, Gower.

Hill, T. J. (1980) 'Manufacturing Implications in Determining Corporate Policy', *International Journal of Operations Management*, Vol. 1, No. 1, pp. 3–11.

Hippel, E. von (1988) *The Sources of Innovation*, Oxford, Oxford University Press.

Hoffman, K. (1989) *Information Technology and the Industrialising Countries*, Report to the Department of Trade and Industry, RTP2.

Hollingum, J. (1980) 'Next Move: Flexible Assembly in Large Volumes', in *The Engineer*, 10 April, pp. 46–8.

Holmqvist, U. (1985) 'Programmable Automatic Assembly Station with new ASEA Robot', in Rathmill, K. (ed.) *Robotic Assembly*, Bedford, IFS, pp. 51–9.

Hounshell, D.A. (1984) *From the American System to Mass Production 1800–1932: The Development of Manufacturing Technology in the United States*, Baltimore, Johns Hopkins University Press.

Hunt, H. A. & T. L. (1983) *Human Resource Implications of Robotics*, Michigan, Upjohn Institute.

Imai, K., Nonaka, I,. & Takuchi, H. (1985) 'Managing the New Product Process: How Japanese Companies Learn and Unlearn', in Clark, K.B., Hayes, R.H., and Lorenz, C. (eds) *The Uneasy Alliance: Managing the Productivity Dilemma*, Boston, Harvard Business School Press, pp. 337–75.

Industrial Computing (1989) *British Industrial Computing Survey*, October 1987, pp. 33–8.

Ingersoll Engineers (1980) *Industrial Robots*, Bedford, IFS.

——(1984) *The FMS Report*, Bedford, IFS.

Institute of Manpower Studies (IMS) (1984) *Flexible Manning, The Way Ahead*, Report No. 88, Brighton, IMS.

International Federation of Robotics (IFR) (1988) *Industrial Robot Statistics 1987*, Geneva, IFR.

——(1989) *Industrial Robot Statistics 1988*, Geneva, IFR.

IPA (1984) 'Flexible Automated Assembly: A Changing Scene', *Assembly Automation*, Vol. 4, No. 3, pp. 51–4.

——(1988) *Change of Fields of Application for Industrial Robots in Germany*, Stuttgart, IFF–IPA.

Ishitani, H. & Kaya, Y. (1989) 'Robotization in Japanese Manufacturing Industry', *Technological Forecasting and Social Change*, Vol. 35, Nos. 2–3, pp. 97–132.

Ito, Y. (1987) 'Evaluation of FMS: State of the Art Regarding How to Evaluate System Flexibility', *Robotics and Computer Integrated Manufacturing*, Vol. 3, No. 3, pp. 327–34.

Jablonoski, S. (1985) 'Reexamining FMS', *American Machinist*, March, pp. 125–40.

Jacobsson, S. (1986) *Electronics and Industrial Policy: The Case of Computer Controlled Lathes*, London, Allen & Unwin.

Jaikumar, R. (1986) 'Postindustrial Manufacturing', *Harvard Business Review*, No. 6, pp. 69–76.

Japan Industrial Robot Association (JIRA) (1987) *Report on the Survey of Actual Condition of Robot Manufacturers in Japan*, Tokyo, JIRA (in Japanese).

——(1988) *The Specifications and Applications of Industrial Robots in Japan*, Tokyo, JIRA.

Kagono, T. Nonaka, I., Sakaibara, K., and Okumura, A. (1985) *Strategic vs. Evolutionary Management: A US-Japan Comparison of Strategy and Organisation*, Amsterdam, North Holland.

Kaplinsky, R. (1984) *Automation, the Technology and Society*, Essex, Longman.

Karlsson, C., & Carlsson, M., (1989) 'Next Practice in Product Development', *International Motor Vehicle Program Policy Forum*, Cambridge, Mass. Center for Technology, Policy and Industrial Development, MIT.

King, S. (1988) 'Temporary Workers in Britain: Findings from the 1986 Labour Force Survey', *Employment Gazette*, April, pp. 238–47.

Klein, B. (1977) *Dynamic Economics*, Cambridge, Mass., Harvard University Press.

Krafcik, J. F. (1988a) 'European Manufacturing Practice in a World Perspective', *International Motor Vehicle Program Policy Forum*, Boston, Mass., MIT.

——(1988b) 'Complexity and Flexibility in Motor Vehicle Assembly: A Worldwide Perspective', *International Motor Vehicle Program Policy Forum*, Boston, Mass., MIT Press.

——(1989) 'Comparative Analysis of Assembly Plant Automation', *International Motor Vehicle Program Policy Forum*, Boston, Mass., MIT.

Krafcik, J. F. & MacDuffie, J. P. (1989) 'Explaining High Performance Manufacturing: The International Automotive Assembly Plant Study', *International Motor Vehicle Program Policy Forum*, Boston, Mass., MIT Press.

Kuhn, T. S. (1970) *The Structure of Scientific Revolutions*, 2nd edn, Chicago, Chicago University Press.

Lewis, A., Nagpal, B. K., and Watts, P. L. (1984) 'Robotics: Market Growth, Application Trends and Investment Analysis', in *Proceedings of the Institute of Mechanical Engineers*, pp. 34–40, Vol. 199, No. B1.

Lim, S. H. (1986) 'Flexibility in Flexible Manufacturing Systems: A Comparative Study of Three Systems', in Voss, C.A. (ed.) *Managing Advanced Manufacturing Technology*, Bedford, IFS, pp. 125–47.

Lockyer, K. (1983) *Production Management*, 4th edn, Marshfield, Mass., Pitman.

Lynch, P. M. (1977) *An Economic Guideline for the Design of Programmable Assembly Machines*, New York, Society of Mechanical Engineers, Report

No.77-WA/Aut-2.
Makino, H. & Furuya, N. (1985) 'SCARA Robot and its Family', in Rathmill, K. (ed.) *Robotic Assembly*, Bedford, IFS, pp. 13-26.
Makino, H. & Yamafuji, K. (1985) 'State-of-the-Art of Automatic Assembly in Japan', in Rathmill, K. (ed.) *Robotic Assembly*, Bedford, IFS, pp. 63-80.
——(1988) 'Trends in Automatic Assembly in Japan', in Pugh, A. (ed.) *Proceedings of the 9th International Conference on Assembly Automation*, Bedford, IFS, pp. 3-18.
Mandelbaum, M. (1978) 'Flexibility in Decision Making: An Exploration and Unification', Toronto, Canada, Ph.D. thesis, University of Toronto, Department of Industrial Engineering.
Marschak, T. & Nelson, R. (1962) 'Flexibility, Uncertainty & Economic Theory', *Metroeconomica*, Vol. 14, pp. 42-59.
Masuyama, A. (1985) 'Idea and Practice of Flexible Manufacturing Systems of Toyota', in Raouf, A. & Ahmad, S.I. (eds) *Flexible Manufacturing: Recent Developments in FMS, Robotics, CAD/CAM, and CIM*, Amsterdam, Elsevier, pp. 141-52.
McCormick, K. (1986) 'Does Japan Produce Better Engineers?', mimeo, Brighton, University of Sussex.
Matthews, M. (1985) 'A Critical Discussion of the Technological Paradigms and Technological Trajectory Thesis', Brighton, M.Sc. dissertation, SPRU, University of Sussex.
Metalworking Engineering and Marketing (1988a) 'Japan's Inventory of Machine Tools', September, pp. 35-9.
——(1988b) 'MITI Statistical Survey of Machine Tool Inventory', November, pp. 128-35.
Metalworking Production (1983) *Fifth Survey of Machine Tools and Production Equipment in Britain*, London, Morgan-Grampian.
——(1988) *Sixth Survey of Machine Tools and Production Equipment in Britain*, London, Morgan-Grampian.
Mikazaki, H., Sakaguchi, T., Furukawa, M., & Sugino, S. (1988) 'Toyota Group Assembly Experience', *Assembly Automation: Japan vs Europe Forum*, pp. 37-60.
Miller, S. M. (1985a) 'Custom, Batch and Mass Production in the Metalworking Industry', in Ayres, R. U. & Miller, S. M. (eds) *Robotics and Flexible Manufacturing Technologies: Assessment, Impacts & Forecast*, New Jersey, Noyes, pp. 145-84.
——(1985b) 'Impacts of Robotics and Flexible Manufacturing Technologies on Manufacturing Costs and Employment', in Kleindorfer, P.R. (ed.) *The Management of Productivity and Technology in Manufacturing*, New York, Plenum Press, pp. 73-110.
Miller, J. & Grocock, S. (1988) 'Flexible Assembly Needs of Smaller Companies', in Pugh, A. (ed.) *Proceedings of the 9th International Conference on Assembly Automation*, Bedford, IFS, pp. 63-76.

MITI (1988) *Seventh Machine Tool Installation Research Survey*, Tokyo (in Japanese).

Mori, S. (1989) 'Macroeconomic Effects of Robotization in Japan', *Technological Forecasting and Social Change*, Vol. 35, Nos. 2-3, pp. 133-48.

Mortimer, J. & Rooks, B. (1987) *The International Robot Industry Report*, Bedford, IFS.

Muramatsu, R., Ishii, K., & Takahashi, K. (1985) 'Flexibility in Pull and Push Type Production Ordering Systems', in Raouf, A. & Ahmad, S.I. (eds) *Flexible Manufacturing: Recent Developments in FMS, Robotics, CAD/CAM, CIM*, Amsterdam, Elsvier, pp.15-29.

Myrup Andreasen, M. & Ahm, T. (1988) *Flexible Assembly Systems*, Bedford, IFS.

NEDC (1983) *Transferable Factors in Japan's Economic Success*, London, National Economic Development Council.

——(1984) *Flexible Machining Systems*, London, National Economic Development Council.

——(1985) *British Industrial Performance*, London National Economical Development Council

Nevins, J. L. & Whitney, D. E. (1978) 'Computer-Controlled Assembly', *Scientific American*, Vol.238, No. 2, pp. 62-74.

Nevins, J. L. & Whitney, D. E. (1980) 'Assembly Research', *Assembly Automation*, No. 1, Vol. 7, pp. 27-42.

Noble, D. F. (1979) 'Social Choices in Machine Design: The Case of Automatically Controlled Machine Tools', in Zimbalist, A. (ed.) *Case Studies in the Labor Process*, New York, Monthly Review Press.

Northcott, J. (1986) *Robots in British Industry*, London, Policy Studies Institute.

Odagiri, H. (1989) *Industrial Innovation in Japan*, Working Paper No. 70, London, Centre for Business Strategy, London Business School.

OECD (1970) *OECD Economic Surveys: Japan*, Paris, OECD.

——(1983) *Industrial Robots: Their Role in Manufacturing Industry*, Paris, OECD.

——(1988) *OECD Economic Surveys: Japan*, Paris, OECD.

Owen, A. E. (1984) *Flexible Assembly Systems: Assembly by Robots and Computer Integrated Systems*, New York, Plenum Press.

——(1985) *Assembly with Robots*, London, Kogan Page.

PA Consulting Group (1990) *Information Technology: The Catalyst for Change*, London, W. H. Allen & Co.

Pascale, R. T. and Athos, A. G. (1981) *The Art of Japanese Management*, New York, Simon and Schuster.

Pavitt, K. (1986) 'Chips' and 'Trajectories': How Does the Semi-Conductor Influence the Sources and Directions of Technical Change?', in MacLeod, R. (ed.) *Technology and the Human Prospect*, London, Pinter, pp. 31-54.

Penrose, E. T. (1968) *The Theory of the Growth of the Firm*, Oxford, Basil Blackwell.

Perez, C (1983) 'Structural Change and the Assimilation of New Technologies in the Economic and Social Systems', *Futures*, October, pp. 357–75.

Peters, T. (1987) *Thriving on Chaos: Handbook for a Management Revolution*, London, Macmillan.

Pham, D. T. (1985) 'The Changing Face of Assembly Automation', in Heginbotham, W. B. (ed.) *Proceedings of the 6th International Conference on Assembly Automation*, Bedford, IFS, pp. 1–12.

Piore, M. J. (1987) *Corporate Reform in American Manufacturing and the Challenge to Economic Theory*, Workshop on Production Reorganisation and Skills, University of California, Berkeley, BRIE.

Piore, M. J. & Sabel, C. F (1984) *The Second Industrial Divide*, New York, Basic Books.

Porter, M. (1989) *The Competitive Advantage of Nations*, Basingstoke, Macmillan.

Primrose, P. L. & Leonard, R. (1987) 'Financial Aspects of Justifying FMS', mimeo, Manchester, UMIST, Total Technology Department.

Pugh, D. S. (1985) *Organisational Theory*, 2nd edn, Middlesex, Penguin.

Pugh, D. S. & Hickson, D. J. (1976) *Organizational Structure in its Context*, London, Gower.

Raouf, A. & Ahmad, S. I. (1985) *Flexible Manufacturing: Recent Developments in FMS, Robotics, CAD/CAM, CIM*, Amsterdam, Elsevier.

Rathmill, K. (1985) *Robotic Assembly*, Bedford, IFS.

Redford, A. H. & Lo, E. (1986) *Robots in Assembly*, Milton Keynes, Open University Press.

Reich, R. B. (1983) *The Next American Frontier*, Middlesex, Penguin.

Riley, F. J. (1983) *Assembly Automation: A Management Handbook*, New York, Industrial Press.

Riley, F. J. (1984) 'Building Flexibility into your Assembly Systems', *Assembly Engineering*, Vol. 27, No.2, pp. 34–6.

——(1987) 'Flexible Assembly in the United States', in Andreason, M.M. (ed.) *Proceedings of the 8th International Conference on Assembly Automation*, Bedford, IFS.

Robinson, E. A. G. (1958) *The Structure of Competitive Industry*, Cambridge, Cambridge University Press.

Robot News (1986) *Robot News Yearbook 1986*, Tokyo, Antenna House.

Robotic Industries Association (RIA) (1988) *Robotics News*, April.

Rooks, B. (1987) 'Robot Growth Rate Falters in 1986', *Industrial Robot*, Vol.14, No.3, pp.149–51.

Rosenberg, N. (1976) *Perspectives on Technology*, Cambridge, Cambridge University Press.

Roszak, T. (1986) *The Cult of Information*, London, Paladin Grafton.

Rothwell, R. & Gardiner, P. (1988) 'Re-innovation and Robust Designs,

Producer and User Benefits', *Journal of Marketing Management*, Vol. 3, No. 3, pp. 372–87.

Sadamoto, K. (1981) *Robots in the Japanese Economy*, Tokyo, Survey Japan.

Sahal, D. (1981) *Patterns of Technological Innovation*, Reading, Mass., Addison-Wesley.

Saito, M. and Nakamura, S. (1989) 'Impacts of Robotization on the Japanese Economy', *Technological Forecasting and Social Change*, Vol. 35, Nos. 2–3, pp. 167–78.

Scherer, F. M., (1980) *Industrial Market Structure and Economic Performance*, Dallas, Houghton Mifflin.

Schonberger, R. J. (1982) *Japanese Manufacturing Techniques*, New York, Free Press.

——(1987) 'Frugal Manufacturing', *Harvard Business Review*, Vol. 87, No. 5, pp. 95–100.

Schumpeter, J. A. (1987) (1943) *Capitalism, Socialism, and Democracy*, London, Unwin.

Schupp, G (1988) 'Trim Assembly with Robots', *Japan versus Europe Forum*, Bedford, IFS, pp. 1–23.

Scott, P. (1984) *The Robotics Revolution*, Oxford, Basil Blackwell.

——(1986) 'Guidelines for Economic Justification of Flexible Automation', in van Brussel, H. (ed.) *Proceedings of the 16th International Symposium on Industrial Robots*, Bedford, IFS, pp. 1045–55.

Scott, P. & Husband, T. M. (1983) 'Robotic Assembly: Design, Analysis & Economic Evaluation', *Proceedings of the 13th International Symposium on Industrial Robots*, Michigan, Society of Manufacturing Engineers, pp. 5.12–5.29.

Seering, W. (1987) 'Robotics, Numerical Control, and the Computer', in Watanabe, S. (ed.) *Microelectronics, Automation, and Employment in the Automobile Industry*, Chichester, Wiley.

Senker, P (1986) 'Production Organisation in Britain', mimeo, Brighton, SPRU, University of Sussex.

——(1988) *Information Technology and Training in Small Engineering Firms in Japan and England*, Brighton, SPRU, University of Sussex.

Sethi, S. P., Namiki, N., & Swanson, C. L. (1984) *The False Promise of the Japanese Miracle*, Boston, Mass., Pitman.

Simons, G. L. (1980) *Robots in Industry*, Manchester, NCC Publications.

Skinner, W. (1978) *Manufacturing in the Corporate Strategy*, New York, Wiley.

——(1985) *Manufacturing: The Formidable Competitive Weapon*, New York, Wiley.

Slack, N. (1983) 'Flexibility as a Manufacturing Objective', *International Journal of Operations and Production Management*, Vol. 3, No. 3, pp. 4–13.

Smith, D. N. & Wilson, R. C. (1982) *Industrial Robots: A Delphi Forecast of Markets and Technology*, Dearborn Michigan, Society of Manufacturing Engineers.

Sorge, A., Hartmann, G., & Warner, M. (1983) *Microelectronics and Manpower in Manufacturing*, London, Gower.

Statistics Bureau (1985) *Japan Statistical Yearbook*, Tokyo, Prime Minister's Office.

Swann, P. (1988) *Product Competition and the Dimensions of Product Space*, Discussion Paper in Economics No. 8802, Middlesex, Brunel University.

Swann, P. & Taghavi, M. (1988) *Product Competitiveness and the 'Ideal Consumer': Some Calculations for Consumer Durables*, Discussion Paper in Economics No. 8803, Middlesex, Brunel University.

SWIRA (1988) *Shipments of Industrial Robots to Swedish Industry*, Stockholm, Swedish Industrial Robot Association.

Tanaka, H. (1986) 'The Impact of Robotization on the Industrial Structure in Japan', in van Brussel, H. (ed.) *Proceedings of the 16th International Symposium on Industrial Robots*, Bedford, IFS, pp. 17-25.

Tanaka, N., Nogouchi, T. and Mibka, M. (1985) 'DNC Robots and Minicomputers Make Flexible Assembly Line', in *Proceedings of the 6th International Conference on Assembly Automation*, Bedford, IFS.

Tange, S. (1984) *Survey of Assembly Automation*, Tokyo, Japan Society of Mechnical Engineers (in Japanese).

Taylor, F. M. (1986) 'Sensory Robotic Systems for the Garment and Shoe Industry', in van Brussel, H. (ed.) *Proceedings of 16th International Symposium on Industrial Robots*, Bedford, IFS, pp. 811-29.

Tchijov, C. & Sheinin, A. (1989) 'FMS: Current Diffusion and Main Advantages', *Technological Forecasting and Social Change*, Vol.35, Nos. 2-3 pp. 277-93.

Teece, D. J. (1980) 'Economics of Scale and Scope of the Enterprise', *Journal of Economic Behavior and Organisation*, No. 1, pp. 223-47.

Teece, D. J. (1982) 'Towards an Economic Theory of the Multiproduct Firm', *Journal of Economic Behavior and Organisation*, No. 3, pp. 39-63.

——(1988) 'Technological Change and the Nature of the Firm', in Dosi, G. *et al.* (eds) *Technical Change & Economic Theory*, London, Pinter, pp. 256-81.

Tidd, J. (1986) 'Recent Trends in the Organisation of Production', M.Sc. dissertation, mimeo, Brighton, SPRU, University of Sussex

——(1988a) 'Survey of Robotic Assembly in the UK', mimeo, Brighton, SPRU, University of Sussex.

——(1988b) *The Introduction and Management of Robotic Assembly in the UK: Some Organisational and Skills Implications*, Report to the Engineering Industry Training Board, Brighton, SPRU, University of Sussex.

——(1988c) 'Flexible Manufacturing with Industrial Robots: The UK Experience and Some Policy Implications', in Jarvis, R. A. (ed.) *Proceedings of the International Symposium and Exposition on Robots*, Bedford, IFS, pp. 855-67.

——(1988d) 'Divergent Trends in Robotic Assembly in the UK and Japan', *Assembly Automation*, Vol. 8, No. 4, pp. 211-12.

——(1989) 'Next Steps in Assembly Automation', *International Motor Vehicle Program Policy Forum*, Cambridge, Mass., MIT.

Trevor, M. (1985) *Japanese Industrial Knowledge: Can It Help British Industry?*, London, Policy Studies Institute.

Trist, E. L., Higgin, G. W., and Pollock, A. B. (1963) *Organisational Choice*, London, Tavistock.

US Congress, Office of Technology Assessment (1990) *Making Things Better: Competing in Manufacturing*, OTA-ITE-443, Washington, Government Printing Office.

Ure, A. (1967) (1835) *The Philosophy of Manufactures*, London, Charles Knight.

Voss, C. A. (1985) 'The Management of New Manufacturing Technology, Eight Propositions', paper presented at the *Production Systems Conference INRA*, Le Chesnay, France, pp. 311–30.

——(1988) 'Implementation: A Key Issue in Manufacturing Technology', *Research Policy*, Vol. 17, No. 2, pp. 55–64.

Ward, D. (1980) 'How Robots Can Put the Job Together', in *The Engineer*, 10 April, pp. 48–53.

Warnecke, H. J., Schraft, R. D., Schweizer, M. & Walther, J. (1983) 'Application of Industrial Robots for Assembly Operations in the Automotive Industry', *Proceedings of the 13th International Symposium on Industrial Robots and Robots 7*, Chicago, Illinois.

Watanabe, S. (1987) *Microelectronics, Automation and Employment in the Automobile Industry*, Chichester, Wiley.

Weiner, S. A. (1985) 'Perspectives in Automotive Manufacturing', in Kleindorfer (ed.) *The Management of Productivity and Technology in Manufacturing*, New York, Plenum Press.

Wheelwright, S. C. (1978) 'Reflecting Corporate Strategy in Manufacturing Decisions', *Business Horizons*, February, pp. 57–65.

White, B. (1983) *Industrial Robots: A Survey of the Japanese Experience*, Birmingham, Technology Policy Unit, Aston University.

White, M. & Trevor, M. (1983) *Under Japanese Management*, London, Policy Studies Institute.

Wickens, P. (1987) *The Road to Nissan*, Basingstoke, Macmillan.

Wild, R. (1985) *Management and Production*, Middlesex, Penguin.

Winch, G. (1983) *Information Technology in Manufacturing Processes*, London, Rossendale.

Woodward, J. (1965) *Industrial Organisation: Theory and Practice*, Oxford, Oxford University Press.

——(1970) *Industrial Organisation: Behaviour and Control*, Oxford, Oxford University Press.

Worthington, G. (1985) 'The Design and Performance of Robotic Systems for PCB Assembly', in Collins, J. A. (ed.) *Robotic Trends: Proceedings of the 8th Annual British Robot Association Conference*, Bedford, IFS.

Yamafuji, K. & Makino, H. (1987) 'Study on Flexible Assembly Automation', in Andreasen, M. M. (ed.) *Proceedings of the 8th International Conference on Assembly Automation*, Bedford, IFS, pp. 1–20.

Yamauchi, Y. (1988) 'Application and Evaluation of Robots in Nissan', in R. A. Jarvis (ed.) *Proceedings of the International Symposium and Expostion on Robots*, Bedford, IFS, pp. 189–208.

Yonemoto, K. (1986) 'Robotization in Japan: an Examination of the Socio-Economic Impacts of Industrial Robots', *International Journal of Technology Management*, Vol. 1, No. 1, pp. 179–96.

——(1987) *General View and Future Outlook of Industrial Robots in Factory Automation*, Tokyo, JIRA.

Index